# High Energy Nuclear Physics

## W. O. LOCK

This book deals with pion physics, that is, pion scattering by nucleons, the photo-production of pions, and pion production by nucleons, and with nucleon-nucleon and nucleon-complex nucleus interactions in the energy region above 100 MeV.

It is based on lectures given to first year post-graduate students in nuclear physics at Birmingham University. It should be of especial value to such students and also to final year undergraduates with an interest in nuclear physics.

The author is Lecturer in Physics at Birmingham University.

*With 4 halftone plates and line illustrations in the text.*

# HIGH ENERGY
# NUCLEAR PHYSICS

—

### W. O. LOCK

Ph.D., F.Inst.P.
*Lecturer in Physics*
*University of Birmingham*

LONDON: METHUEN & CO LTD
NEW YORK: JOHN WILEY & SONS INC

*First published 1960*
*© 1960 W. O. Lock*
*Printed in Great Britain*
*by Butler & Tanner Ltd*
*Frome & London*
*Cat. No. (Methuen) 4071/U*

# Contents

# Preface

This book is based on lectures, given at Birmingham University for the past three years, to first year postgraduate students in nuclear physics. It is intended to be an introduction to the subject; an attempt has been made, therefore, to explain the concepts and principles in some detail. An elementary knowledge of quantum mechanics is assumed; when necessary reference is made to the standard texts by Schiff (*Quantum Mechanics* – McGraw Hill) and Fermi (*Nuclear Physics* – University of Chicago Press). The important topics of high energy electron scattering and of strange particles have been excluded, partly to keep the book of reasonable size and partly because excellent review articles on both these subjects have appeared in the last two years.

I have drawn freely from the standard works on the subject, and these are listed in the Bibliography at the end of each Chapter.

My thanks are due to my colleagues Dr A. P. Batson, Dr C. J. Batty, Dr S. J. Goldsack and Dr D. H. White for permission to use material from lectures given by them; to Dr A. C. L. Barnard, Dr P. J. Duke, Dr P. V. March and Dr H. Muirhead for their comments on a preliminary draft of the manuscript; Mr J. S. Lilley and Dr M. Schneeberger kindly helped with the proof reading, while Dr Batty drew the figures.

This book would not have been completed without the considerable help that I have received from past and present members of the Department of Mathematical Physics at Birmingham. Professor R. H. Dalitz gave me detailed comments on the first draft of the manuscript and elucidated many points for me; Dr S. F. Edwards is largely responsible for the theoretical parts of Chapters III, IV and V, and I have had the benefit of many useful discussions with him; Dr G. E. Brown kindly read the manuscript of the last three chapters; Dr P. T. Matthews assisted me with Chapter VII and gave me much encouragement in the early stages of the writing.

I must also express my thanks to the authors and publishers who have given permission for the use of figures and photographs; acknowledgment is made in the caption to the revelant figure or plate. Lastly, my thanks are due to Mrs M. Appleton for her patient typing and retyping of the manuscript.

*Birmingham*
*June* 1959

W. O. LOCK

# Illustrations

# Illustrations

# CHAPTER 1

# Introduction

Since 1932, following the discovery of the neutron by Chadwick, it has been realized that nuclei are composed of neutrons and protons. The central problem of nuclear physics has therefore been the investigation of the nature and origin of the forces which bind the protons and neutrons together to form a nucleus. Already in 1932 it had been realized that there were important limitations on the nature of the nuclear force, implied by certain properties of nuclei. Studies of the mass defects of nuclei, and their variation with atomic number, showed that the binding energy of a nucleon (the generic term covering both a neutron and a proton) in a nucleus is approximately constant throughout the periodic table. This fact indicates that the nuclear forces are saturated.

Secondly, the magnitude of the binding energy is found to be large, and equal to about 8·5 MeV per nucleon. This immediately tells us that the nuclear forces are very strong compared with electromagnetic forces or gravitational forces. Quantitatively, the strength of the electromagnetic interaction may be expressed in terms of a dimensionless coupling constant $e^2/\hbar c \simeq 1/137$ ($\hbar = h/2\pi$), while the gravitational interaction can be characterized by a dimensionless coupling constant $Gm^2/\hbar c \simeq 2 \times 10^{-39}$ where $G$ is the gravitational constant and $m$ is the mass of the proton. The strength of the nuclear forces, which is implied by a binding energy of several MeV per nucleon, is characterized by a coupling constant $g^2/\hbar c \sim 1$.

The range of nuclear forces is known to be rather small, that is, two nucleons only exert a force on each other when they are closer than about $10^{-13}$ cm. This information comes from a number of sources. For example, Wigner showed that the concept of a short-range force could give an explanation for the relatively low binding energy of the deuteron (2·2 MeV) compared with that of the α-particle

(27·7 MeV). This low binding energy for the deuteron could be due to a neutron–proton force which is strongly attractive and of short range, or to a force which is less strongly attractive but of longer range. More precisely, it is the product of the depth of the potential and of the square of its radius which is roughly determined (for given potential shape) by the low binding energy of the deuteron. The high binding energy observed for the α-particle cannot then be obtained with the relatively weak forces of long range, compatible with the deuteron, but requires the strongly attractive short-range possibility, with the four nucleons packed closely together.

Information on the character of the nuclear forces may be obtained from an analysis of nucleon–nucleon scattering experiments, and this subject is dealt with in more detail in Chapter VII. In particular, neutron–proton scattering experiments at energies above 40 MeV show that there is a high probability for the struck protons, initially at rest, to emerge in the forward direction. This can be readily understood only if the force between neutron and proton has a 'charge exchange' character, so that the incident neutron may go on as a proton after a relatively small momentum transfer.

These characteristics of nuclear forces suggest that a convenient starting point for the theory of nuclear binding is to consider the analogy with chemical binding. In particular the homopolar bond, typified by the hydrogen molecule, is known to be an exchange force. The hydrogen molecule is saturated in the sense that a third hydrogen atom would not be strongly attached to the two atoms which already comprise the molecule, and which are known to be relatively tightly bound. An assembly of many hydrogen atoms has a total binding energy approximately equal to the number of molecules present, and therefore proportional to the number of atoms present. The correct dependence of the nuclear binding energies on the number of particles in the nucleus will be obtained if it is assumed that the forces between nucleons have similar characteristics to the forces of homopolar chemical binding.

The exchange nature of the homopolar bond is associated with the fact that, from the quantum viewpoint, one cannot tell which electron is associated with which atom in the molecule. This is sometimes expressed by saying that the two electrons are continually being exchanged by the two atoms of the molecule. In fact, the molecular exchange force is proportional to the probability for electron exchange taking place. The neutron–proton scattering experiments at 40 MeV could be readily explained in terms of a nuclear exchange force in which charge was transferred from one nucleon to the other in the exchange process.

The hypothesis that nuclear forces had an exchange character was first put forward in 1932 by Heisenberg. However, the origin of these exchange forces was at that time quite unclear. The only interaction then known to change the charge of a nucleon was the beta-decay interaction, an exceedingly weak interaction whose coupling strength may be specified by a dimensionless parameter of order $10^{-14}$. To account for a binding energy as much as 8 MeV per nucleon one needs an interaction characterized by a dimensionless coupling constant $g^2/\hbar c$ of the order of unity. No such interaction was known in 1932.

A decisive advance was made by Yukawa in 1935. It is well known that the interaction between two electrically charged particles can be described in quantum mechanical terms by saying that one particle emits a photon (a zero mass quantum) which is subsequently absorbed by the second particle. In an analogous way Yukawa pictured the strong nucleon–nucleon interaction in terms of one nucleon emitting a quantum which is promptly absorbed by the other nucleon. The short-range nature of the nucleon–nucleon force implies that these quanta have a finite mass; in fact their mass may be deduced from a knowledge of the range of the force, the range $10^{-13}$ cm corresponding to a mass value of $\sim 400$ $m_e$ (see p. 5). For this reason the quanta were termed mesons, a generic term for particles of mass intermediate between that of the electron and that of the proton. We now know that there exist in nature several mesons, of different masses and lifetimes. However, only one of these particles appears to be intimately connected with nuclear forces, and this is the pi-meson, or pion. Therefore in this book we shall only be concerned with pions and nucleons.

Suppose we represent a neutron by the letter $n$, a proton by $p$, and a pion by $\pi^+$, $\pi^-$ and $\pi^0$, depending on its electric charge. We can then write down the interaction between two nucleons via intermediate pions as, for example,

$$n_1 \longrightarrow n_1 + \pi^0 \quad \text{and then} \quad \pi^0 + p_2 \longrightarrow p_2$$

where the subscripts refer to nucleons at positions 1 and 2. In this case a neutron and a proton interact but remain as a neutron and a proton respectively. Similarly

$$p_1 \longrightarrow n_1 + \pi^+ \quad \text{and then} \quad \pi^+ + n_2 \longrightarrow p_2$$

and $\quad n_1 \longrightarrow p_1 + \pi^- \quad \text{and then} \quad \pi^- + p_2 \longrightarrow n_2$

In these cases the exchange of a charged pion exchanges the charge of the two nucleons. It is clear that the force associated with the neutral pion does not change the charge of the nucleons. There is evidence that the nuclear forces involves both non-charge exchange and charge exchange forces (Chapter VII), which indicates that any practical meson theory of nuclear forces must involve both charged and neutral particles.

We may therefore regard nucleons as sources of the meson, or pion, field, in the same way that electric charges are sources of the electrostatic field. The force between two nucleons, in terms of this field, as distinct from the particle picture, is due to the action of the field produced by one nucleon on the second nucleon. This is the exact analogue of the description of the electrostatic force between two charges in terms of the action of the electric field, produced by the one charge, on the second charge. The relationship between the range of the force and the mass of the field quantum can be derived by means of the following illustration. The relativistic relation between the total energy, $E$, the momentum $p$, and the mass $m$, of a particle is

$$E^2 - p^2c^2 - m^2c^4 = 0 \qquad (1.1)$$

Replace $E$ by $+i\hbar\, \partial/\partial t$ and $p$ by $-i\hbar\nabla$, according to the usual rules of quantum mechanics. This substitution gives

$$- \hbar^2\frac{\partial^2}{\partial t^2} + \hbar^2\nabla^2c^2 - m^2c^4 = 0 \qquad (1.2)$$

Let us now introduce a function $\phi(\mathbf{r},\, t)$ which has the significance of a potential and which we may regard as the field variable. Thus

$$\left(\nabla^2 - \frac{1}{c^2}\frac{\partial^2}{\partial t^2} - \frac{m^2c^2}{\hbar^2}\right)\phi = 0$$

and for convenience we may put $K = mc/\hbar$ so that

$$\left(\nabla^2 - \frac{1}{c^2}\frac{\partial^2}{\partial t^2} - K^2\right)\phi = 0 \tag{1.3}$$

The time independent form of this equation is

$$(\nabla^2 - K^2)\phi = 0 \tag{1.4}$$

which may be compared with that of a static electric field which is

$$\nabla^2\phi = 0 \tag{1.5}$$

and whose solution is

$$\phi = e/r \tag{1.6}$$

for a point charge at the origin. The solution of (1.4) is readily shown to be

$$\phi = g\frac{e^{-Kr}}{r} \tag{1.7}$$

where $g$ is a constant which has the dimensions of an electric charge, and which can be referred to as the nucleon strength, or as the coupling constant appropriate to the interaction. $\phi$ may be regarded as the potential associated with the nuclear force field, with the form $\phi = g\dfrac{\exp(-Kr)}{r}$ to be compared with the electrostatic potential $e/r$. The energy of a second nucleon due to this potential field is given by $g\phi$, so that the interaction energy between two nucleons separated by a distance $r$ has the form $g^2\exp(-Kr)/r$. The exponential character of this interaction energy corresponds to a characteristic range $r_0 = 1/K = \hbar/mc$. Now from a study of the deuteron by Wigner, and from the analysis of $n$–$p$ scattering data at low energies, it has been deduced that the range of the nuclear force is of the order of $10^{-13}$ cm. If $r_0$ is taken to be $10^{-13}$ cm, then $m \sim 400m_e$; this value gives the order of magnitude of the mass necessary for the quanta of the meson field, that is, of the pions. Further, with this value of the range of the force, the coupling parameter $g^2/\hbar c$ is required to have a value of order unity in order to fit the known strength of nuclear forces.

It has already been noted that the line of thought followed by Yukawa runs closely parallel to the quantum-mechanical treatment of the electromagnetic field. However, the quanta of the meson field can also carry charge, whereas the quanta of the electromagnetic field are of zero mass and zero charge. Quantum electrodynamics is known to give an excellent description of almost all electromagnetic phenomena. The quantum mechanics of the nuclear field has turned out to be much more difficult to handle than quantum electrodynamics.

## Mesons

A single stationary nucleon cannot emit or absorb a meson with conservation of energy and momentum. However, the uncertainty principle allows energy conservation to be violated over short time intervals, a violation of energy conservation by an amount $\Delta E$ being permitted for a time $\Delta t$, provided that $\Delta E . \Delta t \sim \hbar$. For the emission of a pion by a nucleon the magnitude of the violation of energy conservation $\Delta E$ is about 140 MeV, that is, the energy equivalent of the rest mass of the pion; $\Delta t$ is then $\leqslant 4 \times 10^{-24}$ sec. In this time the meson may travel a distance at most of order $c \times \hbar/m_\pi c^2 = \hbar/m_\pi c$. Thus a stationary nucleon will be surrounded by a cloud of virtual mesons, continually being emitted and re-absorbed. The mesons of this cloud are referred to as virtual because they can be present only over the exceedingly short time intervals ($\leqslant \hbar/m_\pi c^2$) permitted by the uncertainty principle, and are bound to the nucleon, extending at most to distances of order $\hbar/m_\pi c$ from the centre of the nucleon. The presence of this cloud of virtual charged and neutral mesons extends the charge of the proton to a finite extent; it gives the proton charge distribution a finite size of order $\hbar/m_\pi c$ and this has been verified by direct observations on the scattering of 600 MeV electrons from protons at Stanford. Also associated with this cloud of mesons are currents which contribute to the magnetic moment of the proton, bringing this to the value of $+2\cdot79$ nuclear magnetons from the value $+1$ expected for a simple Dirac particle of spin $\frac{1}{2}$. Similarly for the neutron, the meson cloud gives rise to the magnetic moment of $-1\cdot91$ nuclear magnetons observed.

When two nucleons collide, the momentum that is transferred from the one to the other may be visualized as being carried by the exchange of a virtual meson. If the available energy in the $C$-system is greater than the meson rest mass then a free meson may be created, which can be detected by conventional means at large distances from the point of collision. Yukawa pointed out that it would not be surprising if the free meson were unstable since there are lighter particles known, the electron, the neutrino and the photon, to which the meson might transform with a release of energy. Further, the meson is strongly coupled to nucleons, which are known to undergo the beta-decay process, and Yukawa suggested a specific model for meson decay on this basis, according to which the free meson would have a lifetime $\sim 10^{-8}$ sec in its rest system.

At the time at which Yukawa wrote, such unstable intermediate mass particles had not been observed, but in the years immediately before the war much cosmic ray evidence accumulated for their existence. In particular the cloud chamber work of Anderson and Neddermeyer (1937, 1938) and of Street and Stevenson (1937) suggested that at mountain altitudes there was a considerable flux of penetrating particles of mass around $200m_e$. The instability of these penetrating particles was at first deduced from the so-called 'absorption anomaly'. It was found that the absorption of the particles in a given mass of solid absorber was less than that in the same mass of air, and this difference was interpreted as the extra contribution arising from the particles decaying while traversing the long air path.

The decay of one of these particles was first observed directly in a cloud chamber photograph in 1940, when it was found that the charged decay product was an electron. This appeared to be in accord with the model suggested by Yukawa. However, the lifetime of these particles was directly determined by a counter experiment in the same year and was found to be $2 \cdot 15 \times 10^{-6}$ sec. Despite the disagreement with Yukawa's predicted lifetime, the correspondence between the observed and calculated masses led to the tentative identification of these cosmic ray particles with the mesons postulated in Yukawa's theory.

The classic experiments of Conversi, Pancini and Piccioni in 1945–7 threw considerable doubt on this assumption. These workers showed that the negative cosmic ray mesons had a very weak nuclear interaction with matter; in fact, when the particles were brought to rest in a solid material of low atomic number some of them decayed instead of interacting with the nearest positive nucleus. On the Yukawa hypothesis the combined effects of Coulomb and nuclear attraction should always have resulted in absorption of the negative meson. No absorption is expected of course, for the positive meson, for the Coulomb repulsion will prevent it from getting close enough to a nucleus for the attractive nuclear force to become important.

This result, together with other cosmic ray data, led Sakata and Inoue (1946) and, independently, Bethe and Marshak (1947) to suggest that there were two mesons, one the parent of the other. The nuclear force meson, or Yukawa particle, was postulated to be the parent meson, which subsequently decayed to the meson observed by the cosmic ray workers. This prediction was strikingly confirmed by the photographic emulsion work of Lattes, Muirhead, Occhialini and Powell (1947). These authors observed events in emulsions exposed at high altitudes which they interpreted as the decay at rest of a positive heavy meson ($m \sim 300m_e$) into a light meson ($m \sim 200m_e$). The energy of the secondary meson was found to be a constant, implying a two body decay process; it was subsequently shown that the associated neutral particle was a neutrino. In the more sensitive emulsions that became available later, the lighter meson was seen to decay, at rest, into a positive electron which, on the average, took one third of the available energy. This suggested that the decay process involved three particles; the two neutral particles have been shown to be neutrinos. The heavier meson was designated pi ($\pi$) and the lighter particle mu ($\mu$). In this book we shall employ the term pion for the pi-meson and muon for the mu-meson. The two decay sequences can be written

$$\pi^{\pm} \longrightarrow \mu^{\pm} + \nu$$
$$\mu^{\pm} \longrightarrow e^{\pm} + \nu + \nu$$

where $\nu$ represents a neutrino. On the basis of Yukawa's ideas one would expect a $\pi \longrightarrow e$ decay process, but recent experiments give a value of greater than $10^4$ for the ratio of the decays $(\pi \longrightarrow \mu)/(\pi \longrightarrow e)$. The place of the mu-meson amongst the elementary particles, and the significance of the pi–mu decay, is not yet understood.

Events were also seen by Lattes *et al.* which were interpreted as the capture at rest of negative pions by nuclei, leading to the partial or complete, disruption of the nucleus. In fact, an event of this type was observed by Perkins before the positive pi–mu decay was seen. It was clear from these observations that the pion had a strong interaction with nuclei; the positive pions decay when they come to rest in emulsion for the Coulomb repulsion keeps them away from any nearby nucleus. Both positive and negative pions decay to muons if they decay in flight. An early cosmic ray experiment showed that the lifetime of the pion was of the order of $10^{-8}$ sec. This was confirmed when pions were first created under laboratory conditions in 1948, using the 380 MeV $\alpha$-particle beam of the Berkeley synchro-cyclotron.

Prior to the operation of the large accelerators, much cosmic ray evidence pointed to the existence of a neutral meson, which decayed to two or more gamma-rays. Its existence was not finally proved until experiments were carried out at Berkeley on the production of photons from targets bombarded by high energy protons and gamma-rays. The most convincing evidence was afforded by the work of Steinberger *et al.* (1950), who were able to count photons, in co-incidence, which were emitted from a beryllium target bombarded by 330 MeV gamma-rays. A series of experiments showed that the observations could only be interpreted in terms of the production of a neutral pion, which decayed, with a half life of less than $10^{-14}$ sec, to two gamma-rays. It should be remarked here that there is no evidence at the present time for the existence of a neutral muon.

It is now known that the pion is certainly the meson that is largely responsible for nuclear forces, although it does not have all the characteristics predicted for it by Yukawa. During the past ten years extensive studies have been made of the production, properties and interactions of pions. In Chapter II the determination of the intrinsic properties of the pion will be described. Chapter III is concerned with outlining some theoretical ideas which will be needed for a full appreciation of some of the later chapters. Chapters IV and V discuss the main pion interactions that are susceptible to theoretical investigation, that is, pion–nucleon scattering and the photo-production of pions from nucleons. The construction of the large accelerators to produce pion beams has meant that high energy proton and neutron beams have been available for experiments. Many studies of nucleon–nucleus and nucleon–nucleon scattering have been carried out, but the intermediate meson link between the nucleons makes the theoretical approach to the subject very difficult. In fact, the data at present can only be analysed in general phenomenological terms. Chapter VI is concerned with nucleon–complex nucleus elastic scattering, while Chapters VII and VIII consider elastic and inelastic nucleon–nucleon scattering respectively. In the remainder of this chapter, a brief survey will be given of present particle accelerators and experimental techniques. An extensive bibliography on these subjects is given on pp. 18–19.

## Accelerators

The main types of accelerator used to obtain nuclear particles with energies above 100 MeV are the synchro-cyclotron and synchrotron for protons and the betatron, synchrotron and linear accelerator for electrons. A full description of the principles of these machines is given in the book by Livingston (1954). Table 1 gives a list of those machines now operating, or under construction, which yield particles with a kinetic energy of more than 100 MeV.

A synchro-cyclotron accelerates $10^{10}$ to $10^{11}$ protons per pulse with a repetition rate of 60 to 250 pulses per second. The internal beam current is therefore of the order of a microampere, and this is sufficient to give a large flux of pions for experimental work. The Carnegie accelerator, for example, gives 500 $\pi^-$ – particles/cm$^2$.sec focused 20 feet from the target. The exact figures depend on the sign of the pion and on its energy; in any beam there is also a contamination of muons of between 5 and 10%. The magnitude of the external proton beam from a synchro-cyclotron depends upon the details of the extraction system but may be as high as 2% of the internal beam ($\sim 4 \times 10^{10}$ particles/cm$^2$.sec, as at Liverpool). The extracted beam is sometimes used to produce a relatively clean meson beam, as is done at the Dubna Laboratory near Moscow (see Fig. 8). The highest energy synchro-cyclotron is now the Berkeley 184″ machine, which has been modified to give protons of 720 MeV.

To obtain protons with energy above several hundred MeV it is more economical to build a proton synchrotron. Again some

## TABLE 1

| Accelerator and location | | MeV | Date of first operation |
|---|---|---|---|
| *Proton synchro-cyclotrons* | | | |
| McGill, Canada | | 100 | 1949 |
| Harvard, U.S.A. | | 160 | 1949 |
| Orsay, France | | 165 | 1958 |
| Harwell, U.K. | | 175 | 1949 |
| Uppsala, Sweden | | 192 | 1951 |
| Rochester, U.S.A. | | 240 | 1948 |
| Berkeley, U.S.A. | | 190 (d) 380 ($\alpha$) | 1946 |
| | | 350 (p) | 1949 |
| | to | 720 (p) | 1957 |
| Columbia, U.S.A. | | 400 | 1950 |
| Liverpool, U.K. | | 410 | 1954 |
| Dubna, U.S.S.R. | | 280 (d) 560 ($\alpha$) | 1949 |
| | to | 680 (p) | 1953 |
| Carnegie Institute of Technology, U.S.A. | | 450 | 1951 |
| Chicago, U.S.A. | | 460 | 1951 |
| CERN, Geneva | | 600 | 1958 |
| *Proton synchrotrons* | | | |
| Birmingham, U.K. | | 1000 | 1953 |
| Brookhaven, U.S.A. | | 1000 | 1952 |
| | to | 3000 | 1954 |
| Delft, Holland* | | 1000 | 1960 |
| Saclay, France | | 3000 | 1958 |
| Princeton, U.S.A.* | | 3000 | 1960–1 |
| Berkeley, U.S.A. | | 6300 | 1954 |
| Harwell, U.K.* | | 7000 | 1961–2 |
| Moscow, U.S.S.R.* | | 7000 | — |
| Dubna, U.S.S.R. | | 10000 | 1957 |
| Canberra, Australia* | | 10600 | 1960– |
| Argonne, U.S.A.* | | 12500 | 1960– |
| Brookhaven, U.S.A.* | | 30000 | 1960 |
| CERN, Geneva | | 28000 | 1959 |
| *Electron betatrons* | | | |
| Electric Steel Foundry Co., U.S.A. | | 100 | — |
| G.E.C., U.S.A. | | 100 | 1943 |
| Chicago, U.S.A. | | 100 | 1950 |

\* Under construction; therefore the date of operation is the expected date.

## TABLE 1 (*cont.*)

| Accelerator and location | MeV | Date of first operation |
|---|---|---|
| *Electron betatrons* (*cont.*) | | |
| Tomsk, U.S.S.R. | 100 | — |
| Illinois, U.S.A. | 340 | 1950 |
| *Electron synchrotrons* | | |
| Berne, Switzerland | 100 | — |
| Michigan, U.S.A. | 100 | 1952 |
| Naval Research Lab., U.S.A.* | 100 | — |
| Oxford, U.K. | 125 | 1952 |
| Leningrad, U.S.S.R. | 150 | — |
| National Bureau of Standards, U.S.A. | 180 | 1954 |
| Tokyo University, Japan | 200 | — |
| Moscow, U.S.S.R. | 200 | — |
| Moscow, U.S.S.R. | 250 | 1949 |
| G.E.C., U.S.A. | 300 | 1954 |
| Purdue, U.S.A. | 340 | 1952 |
| Glasgow, U.K. | 340 | 1954 |
| Berkeley, U.S.A. | 345 | 1948 |
| Massachusetts Institute of Technology, U.S.A. | 350 | 1950 |
| Cornell, U.S.A. | 300 | 1953 |
| to | 1000 | 1957 |
| California Institute of Technology, U.S.A. | 500 | 1952 |
| to | 1200 | 1957 |
| Bonn, Germany | 500 | 1959 |
| Moscow, U.S.S.R. | 650 | 1958 |
| Tokyo, Japan | 1000 | — |
| Lund, Sweden* | 1200 | 1960 |
| Frascati, Italy | 1000 | 1959 |
| Harvard—M.I.T.* | 5000 | — |
| Armenia, U.S.S.R.* | 3000 | — |
| *Electron linear accelerators* | | |
| Stanford, U.S.A. | 700 | 1950 |
| Orsay, France* | 2000 | 1960 |

* Under construction; therefore the date of operation is the expected date.

A complete list of particle accelerator installations has been given by G. A. Behman, 1958. *Nuclear Instruments*, **3**, 181.

$10^{10}$–$10^{11}$ protons are accelerated in each pulse, but the repetition rate is only 1 in 3 sec (CERN) to 1 in 10 sec (Birmingham). The internal beam current is therefore only of the order of $10^{-3}$ to $10^{-4}$ microamperes. This low beam intensity means that the pion beams are also of low intensity which renders many types of experiment very difficult except by techniques which integrate the data over a long time, such as the emulsion technique. Both the Brookhaven and Berkeley synchrotrons contain straight sections between the four quadrants of the magnet, and it is therefore relatively easy to obtain an extracted proton beam, of comparable intensity to the internal beam. The 25 GeV machines under construction will have internal beam currents of the order of $5 \times 10^9$ particles per pulse with a repetition rate of 12 to 20 pulses per minute (CERN figures). High current machines of moderate energy (3–6 GeV) using improved focusing techniques have been designed recently, while ordinary proton synchrotrons with high repetition rates are under construction; for example, the Princeton 3 GeV machine is designed for 50 pulses a second.

Electron synchrotrons accelerate from $10^8$ to $10^{11}$ electrons in one pulse, with a repetition rate of between 1 and 30 pulses per second. The electron beams have mainly been used to study the photoproduction of mesons by gamma-rays. Intense meson beams cannot be obtained because the cross-sections for their production are small, since an electromagnetic process is involved.

The Stanford linear accelerator can give as many as $10^{13}$ electrons per pulse, and has a repetition rate of 60 pulses a second. It has been extensively used to study the scattering of electrons from different materials. It differs from electron synchrotrons in that the pulse length is only $0.3\ \mu$ sec compared with several microseconds.

## Techniques

The different techniques used to observe moving charged nuclear particles fall into two classes. These are the visual techniques in which the track of an individual particle is observed in some way, and the counting techniques in which a light pulse or electrical pulse is detected, caused by the passage of the particle through a given medium.

Of the visual methods the *cloud chamber* is historically the oldest. The expansion type is not widely used in high energy research with accelerators but finds its chief use in cosmic ray work. The *diffusion cloud chamber*, devised by Langsdorf in 1939, which is continuously sensitive, is better suited for use with accelerators. It is usually filled with hydrogen at a high pressure (e.g. 20 atmospheres) and is employed in conjunction with a magnetic field of 10 or 15 k gauss. By the use of a high magnetic field the momenta of particles can be measured to an accuracy of about 10%. The angles between particle directions can be measured to better than 1°. Ionization measurements are difficult and it is usually only possible to make rough classifications, referred always to some standard particle track (e.g. that of the beam proton) on the same photograph. For particles which are very slow and which stop in the chamber, their range gives a measure of their energy. The diffusion chamber has the disadvantages that the sensitive depth is only 2″ or 3″, although the diameter of the chamber may be as much as 18″ or 20″, and that the density of the hydrogen gas is low, so that the rate of occurrence of events in the chamber is not great.

The *bubble chamber* was suggested, and realized experimentally, by Glaser in 1952. It consists in principle of a superheated liquid under pressure which is allowed to expand to a lower pressure; after a short interval of time, boiling starts along the track of any ionizing particle which may have passed through the chamber after the expansion has taken place. The track of the particle is therefore defined by a row of bubbles, which are photographed. The early chambers were operated with an organic liquid such as pentane but liquid hydrogen chambers have been successfully operated in several laboratories. The main advantage of a hydrogen chamber is that the density of the liquid is 0·070 g/cc compared with about 0·0026 g/cc in a 25 atmosphere diffusion chamber. Thus many events of interest will occur in the chamber with only a low flux of bombarding particles. Most bubble chambers are operated in conjunction with a high magnetic field and the same measurements may be made on the events that are photographed as on diffusion chamber pictures. The high stopping power of the liquid means that a reasonable proportion of the particles from an interaction will be brought to rest in the chamber, typically 10″ in diameter, and their energy determined from their range. Further, if the operating conditions of the chamber are accurately known and controlled it is possible to make fairly accurate ionization measurements.

The present trend seems to be towards the construction of very large liquid hydrogen bubble chambers; for example at Berkeley a chamber of dimensions 72″ × 20″ × 15″ has been constructed. With such large chambers a very high number of events can be photographed in a relatively short time, and the problem of analysing them becomes very serious. To reduce the human labour involved many devices, of varying degrees of complexity, have been constructed; in some the measured data are fed directly to an electronic computer which calculates, for example, track curvatures and angles. The computer is used again to check energy and momentum balance for each event. It is clear that research into high energy nuclear physics with large liquid hydrogen bubble chambers must involve a large number of individuals, working as a team; this appears to be a characteristic feature of the work in this branch of physics.

*Photographic emulsions*, sensitive to charged particles of any energy, have been commercially available since 1948. They have been widely employed both to detect individual particles and to study nuclear disintegrations occurring within them. In the former instance a measurement of the multiple Coulomb scattering of the particle as it traverses the emulsion yields a value of $p\beta$ for the particle, accurate to about 10%, where $p$ is the momentum and $\beta = v/c$. The grain density of the track gives the velocity, $\beta$, of the particle, accurate to about 5% in a typical case, while if the particle stops in the emulsion (density ∼4 g/cc) its energy is determined by the range measurement. The study of nuclear disintegrations occurring in the emulsion has the disadvantage that the target material is fixed as mainly silver, bromine, carbon, nitrogen and oxygen, although some work has been done using the hydrogen present in the emulsion as the target material. Emulsions may be used simply as counters to observe the number of particles scattered at a given angle from some target, and have been extensively used for this purpose at low energies (∼10 MeV). Automatic devices to count the tracks have been devised.

The counting method most widely used at high energies is the *scintillation counter* technique. The principle has been known for many years, but the refinements due to Broser and Kallmann using both organic and inorganic crystals and plastics, and modern photomultiplier tubes, have made this a most versatile and important technique. The crystals are viewed by one or more photomultipliers, and it is common to use several crystals in a line, connected in coincidence or in anticoincidence, thus forming a counter telescope. Range measurements can be carried out by interposing suitable thicknesses of absorber between crystals, while neutrons can be detected by placing a converter, to give knock-on protons, between the first and second crystals, the first crystal being in anticoincidence with those following the converter. The light output from a crystal, as measured by the magnitude of the pulse from the viewing photomultiplier, is a measure of the energy lost by a particle in traversing the crystal. This energy loss is directly proportional to the charge and velocity of the particle. The charge is usually known so that a pulse height analysis can be used to give an estimate of particle velocities. Momentum measurements can be made if the counters (that is, a crystal and its associated photomultiplier and amplifier) are used in conjunction with a magnetic field.

*Čerenkov* counters make use of the fact that radiation in the form of visible light is emitted from a moving charged particle when its velocity is greater than the velocity of light in the medium through which it is passing. This effect was first studied in detail by Čerenkov. Different media clearly have different threshold energies for the emission of Čerenkov radiation, which is detected by suitably placed photo-multipliers. For example, a proton passing through perspex emits this radiation when it has a kinetic energy of more than 325 MeV. The angle at which the radiation is emitted is a function of the velocity of the particle; therefore, by suitably designing the optical system used it is possible to build velocity selecting and velocity measuring Čerenkov detectors. Materials commonly used as radiators include perspex and lead glass.

*Geiger counters*, widely used in low energy nuclear physics, are now only used in high energy work to study radioactivity induced by high energy particles. *Proportional counters* are sometimes used, in place of scintillation counters, in scattering experiments. *Ionization chambers* find their main use as devices to measure beam intensities.

It is important to stress that the most important and useful experiments are those in which hydrogen, or deuterium, is used as the target material. Our present theoretical ideas are only capable of describing simple situations, such as the collisions between pions and nucleons. It will be seen later (Chapters VII and VIII) that even nucleon–nucleon collisions can, as yet, only be described in pheno-menological terms. The experimental techniques which are of most value are therefore those which employ hydrogen as the target material (diffusion cloud chamber, bubble chamber) or those which detect particles emitted from collisions taking place in liquid hydro-gen contained in a vessel. In the former case many thousands of photographs are taken of the collisions which occur in the chamber. Each event is examined and analysed in detail. In the latter case the products of the collisions are detected by counter telescopes, or by photographic emulsions, placed at different angles to the target. In most chapters we shall describe briefly typical experimental arrange-ments that are used to study the processes under discussion.

## BIBLIOGRAPHY

### Nuclear forces and mesons

BETHE, H. A. and MORRISON, P. 1956. *Elementary Nuclear Theory*. Ch. XVIII. Chapman & Hall.

ROSSI, B. 1952. *High Energy Particles*. Ch. 4. Constable.

THORNDIKE, A. M. 1952. *Mesons*. Ch. 1, 2, 3. McGraw-Hill.

WEISSKOPF, V. F. 1956. Chapter in *Recent Advances in Science*, ed. M. H. Shamos and G. M. Murphy. Interscience, New York.

### Accelerators

BLEWETT, J. P. 1956. *Reports on Progress in Physics*, **19**, 37. The Physical Society (proton synchrotrons).

FREMLIN, J. H. and GOODEN, J. S. 1950. *Reports on Progress in Physics*, **13**, 295. The Physical Society.

HAWORTH, L. J. 1956. Chapter in *Recent Advances in Science*, ed. M. H. Shamos and G. M. Murphy. Interscience, New York.

KRAUSE, E. H. 1957. *American Institute of Physics Handbook*. Section 8, 172–201. McGraw-Hill.

LIVINGSTON, M. S. 1954. *High Energy Accelerators*. Interscience.

## TECHNIQUES

HOOPER, J. E. and SCHARFF, M. 1957. *The Cosmic Radiation*. Ch. 2. Methuen.

ROSSI, B. 1952. *High Energy Particles*. Ch. 3. Constable.

### Diffusion cloud chamber

SLATIS, H. 1957. *Nuclear Instruments*, **1**, 213.

SNOWDEN, M. 1953. *Progress in Nuclear Physics*, **3**, 1. Pergamon Press.

YORK, C. M. 1958. *Handbuch der Physik*, **XLV**, 260. Springer.

### Bubble chambers

DODD, C. 1956. *Progress in Nuclear Physics*, **5**, 142. Pergamon Press.

FRETTER, W. B. 1955. *Ann. Rev. Nuc. Sci.* **5**, 145. Annual Reviews Inc. (also covers cloud chambers).

GLASER, D. A. 1958. *Handbuch der Physik*, **XLV**, 314. Springer.

### Emulsions

GOLDSCHMIDT-CLERMONT, Y. 1953. *Ann. Rev. Nuc. Sci.* **3**, 141. Annual Reviews Inc.

POWELL, C. F., FOWLER, P. H. and PERKINS, D. H. 1959. *A Study of Elementary Particles by the Photographic Method*. Pergamon Press.

SHAPIRO, M. M. 1958. *Handbuch der Physik*, **XLV**, 342. Springer.

VOYVODIC, L. 1954. *Progress in Cosmic Ray Physics*, **2**, 219. North-Holland.

### Scintillation counters and fast electronics

BELL, R. E. 1954. *Ann. Rev. Nuc. Sci.* **4**, 93. Annual Reviews Inc.

MOTT, W. E. and SUTTON, R. B. 1958. *Handbuch der Physik*, **XLV**, 86. Springer (and Čerenkov counters).

SWANK, R. K. 1954. *Ann. Rev. Nuc. Sci.* **4**, 111. Annual Reviews Inc.

### Čerenkov detectors

JELLEY, J. V. 1958. *Čerenkov Radiation*. Pergamon Press.

MARSHALL, J. 1954. *Ann. Rev. Nuc. Sci.* **4**, 141. Annual Reviews Inc.

# REFERENCES

ANDERSON, C. D. and NEDDERMEYER, S. H. 1937. *Phys. Rev.* **51**, 884; 1938. ibid. **54**, 88.

BETHE, H. A. and MARSHAK, R. E. 1947. *Phys. Rev.* **72**, 506.

CONVERSI, M., PANCINI, E. and PICCIONI, O. 1947. *Phys. Rev.* **71**, 209.

GLASER, D. A. 1952. *Phys. Rev.* **87**, 665.

LATTES, C. M. G., MUIRHEAD, H., OCCHIALINI, G. P. S. and POWELL, C. F. 1947. *Nature*, **159**, 694.

SAKATA, S. and INOUE, T. 1946. *Prog. Theor. Phys.* **1**, 143.

STEINBERGER, J., PANOFSKY, W. K. H. and STELLER, J. S. 1950. *Phys. Rev.* **78**, 802.

STREET, J. C. and STEVENSON, E. C. 1937. *Phys. Rev.* **52**, 1003.

YUKAWA, H. 1935. *Proc. Phys. Math. Soc. Japan*, **17**, 48.

# CHAPTER II

# The Properties of the Pion

—

In this chapter the determination of the main intrinsic properties of the charged and neutral pions will be discussed, that is, their masses, lifetimes, spin and parity. The work on the masses and lifetimes will be briefly mentioned only since it is well described in several texts (e.g. Rossi, 1952). The determination of the spin and parity involves some theoretical arguments and will therefore be treated in greater detail.

### The conservation laws

The conservation laws that are of importance for the discussion of phenomena that occur in the field of nuclear physics are the conservation of energy, of momentum, of total angular momentum, of parity, and of charge. The first two follow from the postulate that the interactions within a given system are invariant under Lorentz translations, the third from their invariance under rotation, and the fourth from their invariance under reflection of the co-ordinate axes. It appears that parity is conserved, at least to a good approximation, in processes involving strong interactions, such as are effective in scattering and production of nucleons and pions, and in electromagnetic processes. However, for many of the very weak interactions, such as the beta-decay of the nucleon, or of the muon, it has recently become clear that parity conservation is strongly violated. The conservation of charge, and of the total number of nucleons in all processes, is well established. The latter conservation law arises because if there were a process by which the number of nucleons could change, the nucleons in the given system would steadily decrease in number to zero, releasing a great deal of energy.

The total angular momentum $\mathbf{J}$ is the resultant of the total spin angular momentum $\mathbf{S}$ and the total orbital angular momentum $\mathbf{L}$

(all in units of $h/2\pi$). All three quantities are vectors, and they follow the usual laws of vector addition in quantum mechanics. We denote by $l$, $s$, and $j$ the individual values of these three quantities for any one particle. It has become conventional to summarize the state of a particle or system by writing $^{2S+1}L_J$ where $L = 0, 1, 2 \ldots$ is written as $S$, $P$, $D$ following the spectroscopic notation. The case when $S = 0$ is known as a singlet spin state and that in which $S = 1$ as a triplet state, for the quantity $2S + 1$ gives the number of possible orientations of the spin vector with respect to any specified direction.

The concept of parity arises from a symmetry property of space whereby the physical laws of natural phenomena do not allow a means to distinguish left from right. It occurs naturally in the development of quantum mechanics but it does not appear to have a direct physical analogue. The parity of a given state may be defined as a quantity that describes the behaviour of the wave function of the state with respect to a reflection of the coordinate axes, that is when $x$ is changed to $-x$, $y$ to $-y$ and $z$ to $-z$. In the reflected axes a wave function representing a non-degenerate state of definite energy will have the same form as in the original axes, but may have either the same sign or the opposite sign as the original wave function, corresponding to *even* or *odd* parity respectively for the given system. If the energy eigenvalue is degenerate then it is convenient to choose combinations of wave functions which are even or odd with respect to reflections of the axes. It may readily be shown that the orbital angular momentum component of a wave function has even (or positive) parity for $l$ even ($S$, $D \ldots$ waves) and odd (or negative) parity for $l$ odd ($P$, $F \ldots$ waves) (e.g. Schiff, pp. 73–4).

In any strong reaction the *total* angular momentum of the interacting system is conserved, and the *total* wave function, which describes the initial and final states of the system, always remains even or odd with respect to reflections according as it is initially even or odd. This latter condition is usually expressed by saying that parity must be conserved. In order that parity may be conserved in those strong interactions which involve the creation or disappearance of a particle (e.g. a meson), it is necessary to introduce the concept of the *intrinsic parity* of a particle. A particle is said to have even or odd intrinsic parity depending on whether or not the wave function, describing it in position and time, changes sign on reversal of the coordinate axes. Now, the absolute sign of a wave function has no physical significance, for the square of the wave function represents the observable quantity. But consider a system which changes by the creation or destruction of a particle of given intrinsic parity. The effect of this change can be observed, for the spatial parity of the residual system adjusts itself to compensate for the change in parity caused by the formation or absorption of the particle. Thus, for the case of the pion, intrinsic parity is a quantity that must be determined experimentally. It is conventional to define the intrinsic parity of protons, neutrons and negative electrons to be even.

One further point may be made here. For a state consisting of two identical particles of integer spin (bosons), interchanging the positions of the two particles (in their C-system) is equivalent to changing the signs of all their relative coordinates. The first operation must leave the sign of the wave function unchanged, and therefore the two bosons must be in a state of relative motion of even parity. States of relative motion of odd parity are forbidden to systems consisting of two identical bosons.

## Mass

The most accurate method employed to determine the mass of the charged pions has been that of momentum–range analysis; the momentum of a pion, created in a thin target and incident on a nuclear emulsion, is determined by the curvature of its trajectory in a magnetic field, while its range in the emulsion can also be expressed in terms of its energy. From these two quantities its mass may be determined. In the actual experiments (Barkas $et$ $al.$, 1956) protons and $\mu$-mesons of the same velocity were allowed to enter the same region of the emulsions as the pions and mass ratios were obtained. Taking the mass of the proton to be $1836 \cdot 1 m_e$ (Du Mond and Cohen, 1953) the results obtained from a series of experiments were

$$m(\pi^+) = 273 \cdot 3 \pm 0 \cdot 2 m_e; \quad m(\mu^+) = 206 \cdot 9 \pm 0 \cdot 2 m_e$$
$$m(\pi^-) = 272 \cdot 8 \pm 0 \cdot 3 m_e$$

A measurement by Crowe and Phillips (1954) of the gamma-ray energy spectrum from the reaction $\pi^- + p \longrightarrow n + \gamma$, for negative pions captured at rest, gives $m(\pi^-) = 272 \cdot 7 \pm 0 \cdot 3 m_e$, in excellent agreement with the value obtained by Barkas *et al.*

The mass of the $\pi^0$-meson has been obtained from a measurement of the energy release in the reaction which takes place when $\pi^-$-mesons are captured at rest by hydrogen. The mesons first fall into a Bohr orbit about the proton and are then captured, when the following reactions are observed to take place

$$\pi^- + p \rightarrow n + \gamma \tag{2.1}$$

$$\pi^- + p \rightarrow n + \pi^0 \rightarrow n + 2\gamma \tag{2.2}$$

Of course the existence of the reaction (2.2) requires at once that the difference $m(\pi^-) - m(\pi^0) = \delta$ be greater than the neutron–proton mass difference $m(n) - m(p) = \Delta = 1 \cdot 3$ MeV. In fact, a spectrum of gamma-rays with a mean energy of about 70 MeV is observed in addition to the monoenergetic (131 MeV) gamma-rays from (2.1). The width of the spectrum gives a measure of the velocity of the decaying $\pi^0$ and therefore of the energy release in reaction (2.2). This experiment was carried out by Panofsky *et al.* (1951) who obtained a value of $10 \pm 2 m_e$ for the $\pi^-$, $\pi^0$ mass difference. Another measure of the velocity was obtained by Chinowsky and Steinberger (1954a) who determined the degree of angular correlation between the two gamma-rays from the $\pi^0$-decay; they found $\delta = 8 \cdot 8 \pm 0 \cdot 6 m_e$ and thus $m(\pi^0) = 264 \cdot 0 \pm 0 \cdot 7 m_e$.

The ratio of the cross-sections for process (2.2) to that for process (2.1) is known as the Panofsky ratio, P. One would expect this ratio to be approximately of the order of $g^2/e^2 \simeq 137$, since the reaction $\pi^- + p \rightarrow \pi^0 + n$ involves only mesons and nucleons and is a strong reaction, whereas the reaction $\pi^- + p \rightarrow n + \gamma$ involves the weak electromagnetic interaction. In fact, recent experiments, at Liverpool and at Chicago, yield values of P between $1 \cdot 50$ and $1 \cdot 90$. The reaction leading to the $\pi^0$ meson is partially inhibited because it depends on the known weak $s$-wave interaction of pions. This point will be discussed in more detail in Chapter IV.

## Decay processes and lifetimes

A charged pion decays to a $\mu$-meson (muon) and a single neutrino. Recent experiments suggest that the ratio of the number of decays

$\pi \longrightarrow \mu + \nu$ to those of $\pi \longrightarrow e + \nu$ is greater than $10^4$. It appears certain that the nuclear beta-decay process does not arise from an electronic $\pi$-meson decay process. Further, a pseudo-scalar pion (odd parity) could not give the types of beta-decay coupling that are observed. The mean lifetime, $\tau$, for $\pi^+ \longrightarrow \mu^+ + \nu$ has been measured using scintillation counters in conjunction with a fast oscilloscope (e.g. Jakobson *et al.*, 1951) with the result that

$$\tau(\pi^+) = 2.54 \pm 0.11 \times 10^{-8} \text{ sec}$$

Observations of the process $\pi^- \longrightarrow \mu^- + \nu$ in a cloud chamber by Lederman *et al.* (1951) gave

$$\tau(\pi^-) = 2.92 \pm 0.32 \times 10^{-8} \text{ sec}$$

It is usually assumed that

$$\tau(\pi^+) = \tau(\pi^-) = 2.54 \times 10^{-8} \text{ sec.}$$

The predominant decay mode of the neutral pion is to two gamma-rays. An alternative decay process

$$\pi^0 \longrightarrow e^+ + e^- + \gamma \tag{2.3}$$

takes place in about 1 in every 80 decays (Dalitz, 1951), while a decay to two electron pairs is predicted to occur 1 in every 29,000 cases. The principal information on the lifetime has come from a study of events in which the pion transforms according to the scheme (2.3). For example, observations of the distance between the centre of a nuclear disintegration, in a photographic emulsion, and the point of origin of the direct electron pairs suggested that $\tau$ was $5.5 \pm 2.5 \times 10^{-15}$ sec (Anand, 1953). Recently observations have been made of the decay (2.3) of neutral pions arising from the decay of $K_{\pi 2}$ particles. The $K_{\pi 2}$ meson is one of a family of heavy particles of mass around $1000 m_e$, with the decay mode

$$K_{\pi 2}^+ \longrightarrow \pi^+ + \pi^0 \tag{2.4}$$

Although the lifetime for this decay process is $1.2 \times 10^{-8}$ sec, the particles are brought to rest in nuclear emulsions in a time which is of the order of $10^{-11}$ sec. Therefore, the great majority of the decays take place at rest. Harris *et al.* (1957) analysed 14 cases of $K_{\pi 2}$ decays at rest in emulsions, in which the neutral pion decayed by the mode (2.3). The line of flight of the neutral pion is determined by the direction of the positive pion, since the event is a two-body decay at rest. The distance travelled by the neutral pion before decay is therefore given by the distance between the intersection of the tracks of the $K_{\pi 2}$ and $\pi^+$ particles and the intersection of the electron pair with the line of flight of the $\pi^0$-meson (see Fig. 1). The experimental data gave no indication of a displacement of the pair origins from the ending of the K-mesons. It was shown that it should have been possible to detect a decay length of 0·2 micron or greater; this length corresponds to a lifetime of $5 \times 10^{-16}$ sec, which may therefore be taken as an upper limit to the mean life of the neutral pion. The result of Anand may be in error because an electron and a positron which are very close together do not immediately cause sufficient ionization to render silver grains developable. This effect was first suggested by King in 1950 (see Perkins, 1955), and has been investigated theoretically by several authors.

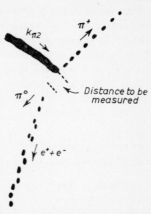

Fig. 1. Schematic drawing of the decay process $K_{\pi 2} \to \pi^+ + \pi^0$ with the $\pi^0$ subsequently decaying via $\pi^0 \to e^+ + e^- + \gamma$

### The spin of the positive pion

The spin of the positive pion has been deduced by applying the principle of detailed balance to the reaction

$$p + p \rightleftharpoons \pi^+ + d \tag{2.5}$$

This principle may be explained in the following way (see Fermi, 1950, pp. 142–6). Suppose we have a box filled with arbitary numbers of particles A, B, C, D, and that the transitions $A + B \rightleftharpoons C + D$ take place. Statistical mechanics states that at equilibrium all possible states of the system, consistent with the specification of the energy of the system, are occupied with equal probability. At equilibrium the number of transitions $A + B \longrightarrow C + D$ per unit time,

equals the number of transitions $C + D \rightarrow A + B$, per unit time.
This is known as detailed balance. The transition rates depend on
the cross-sections for $p + p \rightarrow \pi^+ + d$ and $\pi^+ + d \rightarrow p + p$ and
on the spins of the particles involved. A measurement of the two
cross-sections, at a given centre of mass energy, therefore enables
the spin of the pion to be determined, for the other spins are known.
The necessary equation is derived in the following way. The number
of transitions per unit time, $\omega$, from an initial state, $i$, to a final
state, $f$, for a given reaction, is given by time dependent perturbation theory* as

$$\omega = \frac{2\pi}{\hbar} \mid M \mid^2 \frac{dn}{dE} \qquad (2.6)$$

where $M$ is the matrix element of the perturbation causing the
transition and $dn/dE$ is the energy density of the final states. $M$

has the form $\int \psi_f U \psi_i \, dv$ where $\psi_i$ and $\psi_f$ are the initial and final

state wave functions and $U$ is the interaction energy. The number
of states $dn$ of a particle of momentum between $p$ and $p + dp$,
confined in a box of volume $\Omega$ is

$$dn = \frac{4\pi p^2 \, dp}{(2\pi\hbar)^3} \cdot \Omega$$

(Proved in Fermi (1950), p. 76.)

Further, since $E^2 = p^2 + m^2$ where $E$ is the total energy, and we
use a system of units such that the velocity of light, $c = 1$,

$$dE = v \, dp$$

where $v$ is the velocity of the particle in question in the $C$-system.

Therefore $\qquad \dfrac{dn}{dE} = \dfrac{4\pi p^2}{(2\pi\hbar)^3} \cdot \dfrac{\Omega}{v}$

and $\qquad \omega(i \rightarrow f) = \dfrac{2\pi}{\hbar} \sum_f \mid M(i \rightarrow f) \mid^2 \dfrac{dn}{dE}$

where the $\sum$ is the sum over all final spin states.

Now the cross-section $\sigma_\theta$, at a particular angle, $\theta$, is for the average

* Proved in Schiff, *Quantum Mechanics*, 2nd Ed., p. 199.

over all initial spin states, so that

$$\sigma_\theta(i \longrightarrow f) = \frac{1}{(2s_1{}^i + 1)(2s_2{}^i + 1)} \sum_i \omega(i \longrightarrow f) / \text{flux}$$

where flux = no. per unit volume × velocity, and where $s_1{}^i$, $s_2{}^i$ are the spins of the two initial particles. If we take one incident particle in the volume $\Omega$ then

$$\sigma_\theta(i \longrightarrow f) = \frac{1}{(2s_1{}^i + 1)(2s_2{}^i + 1)} \sum_i \omega(i \longrightarrow f) / v_i \times \frac{1}{\Omega}$$

so that

$$\sum_i \omega(i \longrightarrow f) = \frac{2\pi}{\hbar} \sum_f \mid M(i \longrightarrow f) \mid^2 \frac{4\pi p_f{}^2}{(2\pi\hbar)^3} \cdot \frac{\Omega}{v_f} =$$

$$\sigma_\theta(i \longrightarrow f) \frac{v_i}{\Omega} (2s_1{}^i + 1)(2s_2{}^i + 1)$$

In the reaction $p + p(i) \longrightarrow d + \pi^+(f)$, in which the relative velocity of the $\pi^+$ and $d$ in the final state is $v_f$ and the momentum $q$ (all in the $C$-system), we therefore have

$$\sum_i \omega(i \longrightarrow f) = \frac{2\pi}{\hbar} \sum_f \mid M(i \longrightarrow f) \mid^2 \frac{4\pi q^2}{(2\pi\hbar)^3} \cdot \frac{\Omega}{v_f}$$

$$= \sigma_\theta(p + p \longrightarrow d + \pi^+) \frac{v_i}{\Omega} (2s_p + 1)(2s_p + 1)$$

where $s_p$ is the spin and $v_i$ is the relative velocity of the incident protons (in the $C$-system).

Conversely, we can write

$$\sum_f \omega(f \longrightarrow i) = \frac{2\pi}{\hbar} \sum_i \mid M(f \longrightarrow i) \mid^2 \frac{4\pi p^2}{(2\pi\hbar)^3} \cdot \frac{\Omega}{v_i}$$

$$= \sigma_\theta(\pi^+ + d \longrightarrow p + p) \frac{v_f}{\Omega} (2s_\pi + 1)(2s_d + 1)$$

where $s_\pi$ is the pion spin, $s_d$ the deuteron spin and $p$ is the momentum of the two protons. At the same centre of mass energy we may equate the transition rates and

$$\sum \mid M(i \longrightarrow f) \mid^2 = \sum \mid M(f \longrightarrow i) \mid^2$$

so that, after substituting for $s_d$ and $s_p$

$$\sigma_\theta(p + p \longrightarrow d + \pi^+) = \sigma_\theta(\pi^+ + d \longrightarrow p + p) \times \frac{3(2s_\pi + 1)}{4} \frac{q^2}{p^2} \quad (2.7)$$

Integration over all angles, $\theta$, gives for the total cross-sections

$$\sigma_{\text{total}}(p + p \longrightarrow d + \pi^+)$$
$$= 2\sigma_{\text{total}}(\pi^+ + d \longrightarrow p + p) \times \frac{3(2s_\pi + 1)}{4} \frac{q^2}{p^2} \quad (2.8)$$

The differential and total cross-sections for deuteron production were measured at Berkeley in 1953, for a proton (laboratory) kinetic energy of 341 MeV (Cartwright *et al.*, 1953). This corresponds to a kinetic energy of 21·4 MeV for the positive pion in the centre of mass system. The authors calculated the differential and total cross-sections for the inverse process (using 2.7 and 2.8), for $s_\pi = 0$ and $s_\pi = 1$, and compared them with the experimental results of Durbin *et al.* (1951a, b) and of Clark *et al.* (1951, 1952). This comparison is given in Table 2; although the errors are large it is clear the data strongly suggest that $s_\pi = 0$.

TABLE 2

| Authors | $S_\pi$ | $T_\pi$(MeV) | $\left(\dfrac{d\sigma}{d\Omega}\right)$ for $\pi^+ + d \longrightarrow p + p$ $\times 10^{28}$cm²sterad⁻¹ | $\sigma_{\text{total}} \times 10^{27}$cm² |
|---|---|---|---|---|
| Cartwright *et al.* | 0 | 21·4 | $11 \pm 4$ $(0 \cdot 11 \pm 0 \cdot 06 + \cos^2 \theta)$ | $3 \cdot 0 \pm 1 \cdot 0$ |
| ,, | 1 | 21·4 | $3 \cdot 7 \pm 1 \cdot 3$ $(0 \cdot 11 \pm 0 \cdot 06 + \cos^2 \theta)$ | $1 \cdot 0 \pm 0 \cdot 3$ |
| Clark *et al.* | | 23 (Av) | — | $4 \cdot 5 \pm 0 \cdot 8^*$ |
| Durbin *et al.* | | 25 | $9(0 \cdot 22 + \cos^2 \theta)$ | $3 \cdot 1 \pm 0 \cdot 3$ |

* Assuming an angular distribution $0 \cdot 2 + \cos^2 \theta$.

### The spin of the neutral pion

The spin of the neutral pion cannot be determined directly but Yang (1950) has shown that selection rules for the decay process exist from which the spin may be inferred. We consider here only the two possibilities that the spin is zero or unity; and we use the experimental fact that the predominant decay mode of the neutral pion is to two gamma-rays. The treatment is essentially that given by Matthews (1955).

Consider the neutral pion in its rest system. If it has spin 1, then the final wave function describing the two gamma-rays must be a vector, for the initial wave function must contain the spin and is therefore a vector. The final wave function involves three vectors, $\epsilon_1$ and $\epsilon_2$, the polarization vectors of the two photons and $\mathbf{k}$ their relative momentum. The wave function has to satisfy three conditions: (i) that it is linear in $\epsilon_1$ and $\epsilon_2$, that is, each photon must occur once only; (ii) that it is symmetric for interchange of the two photons, which requires $\epsilon_1 \longleftrightarrow \epsilon_2$ and $\mathbf{k} \longrightarrow -\mathbf{k}$ and (iii) that $\epsilon_1 . \mathbf{k} = \epsilon_2 . \mathbf{k} = 0$ for we have transverse photons with $\epsilon$ and $\mathbf{k}$ perpendicular to each other. The only bilinear vectors that one can construct are

$$\left.\begin{array}{ll}(a) & \epsilon_1 \times \epsilon_2 \\ (b) & (\epsilon_1 . \epsilon_2)\mathbf{k} \\ \text{and} \quad (c) & \mathbf{k} \times (\epsilon_1 \times \epsilon_2)\end{array}\right\} \tag{2.9}$$

The first two are excluded by condition (ii), while the third is excluded by (iii) for $\mathbf{k} \times (\epsilon_1 \times \epsilon_2) = \epsilon_1(\mathbf{k} . \epsilon_2) - \epsilon_2(\mathbf{k} . \epsilon_1)$. The above argument can be generalized for any odd angular momentum.

If we assume spin zero for the $\pi^0$ then the final wave function can either be a scalar or a pseudo-scalar, depending on the intrinsic parity of the meson. We can have

(d) $\epsilon_1 . \epsilon_2$      scalar, positive parity, parallel polarizations of the photons.

(e) $(\epsilon_1 \times \epsilon_2) . \mathbf{k}$ pseudo-scalar, negative parity, perpendicular polarization of the photons.      (2.10)

It is usual, therefore, to take $s = 0$ for the neutral pion, although the above argument does not exclude higher even spins. In principle we could distinguish between (d) and (e) (and thus determine the intrinsic parity of the $\pi^0$ directly) by measuring the polarizations of the two gamma-rays in coincidence. The spin of the $\pi^0$ could also be deduced from a measurement of the correlation between the planes of the two electron pairs from the rare decay mode

$$\pi^0 \longrightarrow e^+ + e^- + e^+ + e^-$$

Unfortunately these are difficult experiments to carry out.

## Parity of the negative pion

The decisive information on the parity of the $\pi^-$-meson comes from a study of the reactions which take place when it is captured from rest in deuterium. Three reactions are energetically possible

$$\pi^- + D \rightarrow n + n \tag{2.11}$$

$$\pi^- + D \rightarrow n + n + \gamma \tag{2.12}$$

$$\pi^- + D \rightarrow n + n + \pi^0 \tag{2.13}$$

It has been shown that the total time for a negative pion to slow down in a liquid deuterium target, to be captured to form a $\pi$-$D$ 'atom', and to reach the $K$-orbit of this 'atom', is not longer than $\sim 10^{-10}$ sec. Further, it has been shown that even in the $2p$ level of the $\pi$-$D$ system, direct nuclear absorption of the pion does not compete with the $2p$-$1s$ radiative transition. Thus, all $\pi^-$-mesons coming to rest in liquid deuterium may be assumed to undergo nuclear capture from an $l = 0$ state. The initial $\pi^- + D$ system therefore has $J = 1$ since only the deuteron spin of 1 contributes to the angular momentum. For reaction (2.11) the two neutrons, being identical particles, can only be in a $^3P_1$ state, this being the only state of total angular momentum 1 allowed by the Pauli principle for two neutrons. Since the deuteron has even parity whilst the $^3P_1$ state has odd parity, it is clear that this reaction (2.11) can occur only if the $\pi^-$-meson has negative intrinsic parity; then both parity and total angular momentum will be conserved.

The original work of Panofsky *et al.* suggested that only 30 % of the $\pi^- - D$ 'atoms' formed gave rise to $\gamma$-rays, that is, that

$$S = \frac{\sigma(\pi^- + D \rightarrow n + n)}{\sigma(\pi^- + D \rightarrow n + n + \gamma)} = 2 \cdot 36 \pm 0 \cdot 74$$

This figure was based on the number of $\pi^- - H$ 'atoms' formed determined in the experiment using hydrogen. This is known since both (2.1) and (2.2) give rise to $\gamma$-rays; it was assumed that the meson flux did not change appreciably when the hydrogen target was replaced by one of deuterium. In later experiments the two neutrons from (2.11) were observed in concidence with the incident pion by means of the recoil protons, or nuclear disintegrations, which they produced in large scintillation crystals (Chinowsky and Steinberger,

1954b). These authors found $S = 1\cdot5 \pm 0\cdot8$. More recent work gives $S = 2\cdot35 \pm 0\cdot35$ (Kuehner *et al.*, 1959). It is clear that (2.11) is allowed, and therefore that the negative pion (and therefore the neutral and positive pions) has negative intrinsic parity. This fact is sometimes expressed by saying that the pion is a pseudo-scalar particle.

Reaction (2.13) is not observed. This is not an unexpected result since either the two neutrons or the $\pi^0$ meson must have $J = 1$, that is $l_\pi = 1$ or $l = 1$ for the two neutrons, irrespective of the parities of the $\pi^-$ and $\pi^0$ mesons. The low available energy (only $2\cdot3$ MeV) makes $l = 1$ very unlikely.

The properties of the pi and mu-mesons are summarized in Table 3.

TABLE 3

| | $\pi^\pm$ | $\pi^0$ | $\mu^\pm$ |
|---|---|---|---|
| Mass in $m_e$ | $273\cdot2 \pm 0\cdot2$ | $264\cdot0 \pm 0\cdot7$ | $206\cdot9 \pm 0\cdot2$ |
| Lifetime in sec. | $2\cdot54 \times 10^{-8}$ | $< 5 \times 10^{-16}$ | $2\cdot261 \pm 0\cdot007 \times 10^{-6}$ |
| Spin | 0 | 0 | $\frac{1}{2}$ |
| Parity | Odd | Odd | Even by definition, not an observable quantity |
| Magnetic moment | 0 | 0 | $2\cdot0048 \pm \cdot0016\dfrac{eh}{4\pi m_\mu c}$ |

BIBLIOGRAPHY

ROSSI, B. 1952. *High Energy Particles*. Ch 4. Constable.

ROSSI, B. 1955. *Nuovo Cimento*, **II** (Ser. x), Supplemento No. 1, 163–71 (conservation laws).

THORNDIKE, A. M. 1952. *Mesons*. Ch. 4, 5. McGraw-Hill.

WICK, G. C. 1958. *Ann. Rev. Nuc. Sci.* **8**, 1 (invariance principles).

REFERENCES

ANAND, B. M. 1953. *Proc. Roy. Soc.* **A220**, 183.

BARKAS, W. H., BIRNBAUM, W. and SMITH, F. M. 1956. *Phys. Rev.* **101**, 778.

CARTWRIGHT, W. F., RICHMAN, C., WHITEHEAD, N. M. and WILCOX, H. A. 1953. *Phys. Rev.* **91**, 677.

CHINOWSKY, W. and STEINBERGER, J. 1954a. *Phys. Rev.* **93**, 586; 1954b. ibid. **95**, 1561.

CLARK, D. L., ROBERTS, A. and WILSON, R. 1951. *Phys. Rev.* **83**, 649; 1952. ibid. **85**, 523.

CROWE, K. M. and PHILLIPS, R. H. 1954. *Phys. Rev.* **96**, 470.

DALITZ, R. H. 1951. *Proc. Phys. Soc.* **A64**, 667.

DU MOND, J. M. and COHEN, E. R. 1953. *Rev. Mod. Phys.* **25**, 691.

DURBIN, R., LOAR, H. and STEINBERGER, J. 1951a. *Phys. Rev.* **83**, 646; 1951b. ibid. **84**, 581.

FERMI, E. 1950. *Nuclear Physics.* University of Chicago Press.

HARRIS, G. G., OREAR, J. and TAYLOR, S. 1957. *Phys. Rev.* **106**, 327.

JAKOBSON, M. J., SCHULZ, A. G. and STEINBERGER, J. 1951. *Phys. Rev.* **81**, 894.

KUEHNER, J. A., MERRISON, A. W. and TORNABENE, S. 1959. *Proc. Phys. Soc.* **73**, 551.

LEDERMAN, L. M., BOOTH, E. T., BYFIELD, H. and KESSLER, J. 1951. *Phys. Rev.* **83**, 685.

MATTHEWS, P. T. 1955. *Reports on Progress in Physics*, **18**, 453. The Physical Society, London.

PANOFSKY, W. K. H., AAMODT, L. and HADLEY, J. 1951. *Phys. Rev.* **81**, 565.

PERKINS, D. H. 1955. *Phil. Mag.* **46**, 1146.

YANG, C. N. 1950. *Phys. Rev.* **77**, 242.

# CHAPTER III

# Fundamental Concepts

In any discussion of the properties and interactions of fundamental particles it is necessary to use certain terms and concepts which are basic to the whole subject. In this chapter are discussed those concepts and mathematical tools which are a necessary background to the topics of the following chapters. The details of the partial wave analysis and the outline of meson field theory may be omitted at a first reading.

## Charge symmetry and charge independence. Isotopic spin

These are two postulates that summarize, in a concise form, our knowledge of the forces which exist between nucleons. *Charge symmetry* states that the nuclear force between two protons is the same as that between two neutrons, provided that in the two cases the particles are in the same spin and orbital angular momentum state. The best evidence for the validity of this postulate comes from mirror nuclei, that is, nuclei of charge Z and Z + 1 but with the same total number of neutrons and protons. For example, the binding energies of $H^3$ and $He^3$, and $C^{13}$ and $N^{13}$, are found to be equal after allowance has been made for Coulomb forces.

*Charge independence* states that the force between any two nucleons is the same, provided again that they are in the same spin and orbital momentum state. This hypothesis was first advanced by Breit and Feenberg (1936) and was based on the experimental equality of *np* and *pp* nuclear forces in the singlet state ($^1S_0$). This result was based on scattering experiments carried out at energies of a few MeV. Evidence for the validity of the hypothesis of charge independence at much higher energies will be discussed in Chapter VIII. Cassen and Condon (1936) therefore suggested describing the two states of the nucleon by a variable analogous to ordinary spin, called the 'Isotopic spin vector, $T$'. We therefore speak of one particle, the nucleon, of isotopic spin $T = \frac{1}{2}$. The two possible states of this particle are given by the possible values of the third component of $T$, namely $T_3 = +\frac{1}{2}$, which is assigned to the proton, and $T_3 = -\frac{1}{2}$ to the neutron. $T_3$ in isotopic spin space is analogous to the $z$ component of spin in ordinary space.

The charge, $q$, of the nucleon may be expressed in terms of $T_3$ by the relation

$$q = T_3 + \frac{1}{2} \tag{3.1}$$

For $b$ nucleons the isotopic spins are combined according to the usual rules of vector addition, and the total charge $Q$ will be given by

$$Q = T_3 + \frac{b}{2} \tag{3.2}$$

For two nucleons the resultant total value of $T$ will be 0 or 1; $T = 1$ with $T_3 = +1$, 0, and $-1$ will correspond to two protons, a neutron and a proton, and two neutrons respectively, while $T = 0$, $T_3 = 0$ will also correspond to a neutron and a proton.

It is found convenient to introduce a specific isotopic spin or charge wave function which may be denoted by $u_p$ for the proton and $u_n$ for the neutron. In the two component notation

$$u_p = \begin{pmatrix} 1 \\ 0 \end{pmatrix}; \quad u_n = \begin{pmatrix} 0 \\ 1 \end{pmatrix} \tag{3.3}$$

where the square of the first component expresses the probability of the particle being a proton and the square of the second that of it being a neutron. For two nucleons, labelled (1) and (2), four isotopic spin wave functions, $\Psi$, can be written down. For two protons and for two neutrons

$$\Psi(p,p) = u_p(1)u_p(2) \tag{3.4}$$

$$\Psi(n,n) = u_n(1)u_n(2) \tag{3.5}$$

respectively. Both of these isotopic spin wave functions are symmetric with respect to interchange of the two particles. The neutron–proton system has two possible wave functions, namely

$$\Psi(n,p) = \frac{1}{\sqrt{2}} \left[ u_p(1)u_n(2) + u_p(2)u_n(1) \right] \tag{3.6}$$

and $\qquad \Psi(n,p) = \dfrac{1}{\sqrt{2}} \ [u_p(1)u_n(2) - u_p(2)u_n(1)]$ $\qquad$ (3.7)

These are derived in an exactly analogous manner to the derivation of the wave functions describing two spin $\frac{1}{2}$ particles (see, for example, Schiff, p. 233). Expression (3.6) is symmetric with respect to interchange of the two particles, while (3.7) is antisymmetric. The three symmetric functions correspond to the three possible values of $T_3$ for the $T = 1$ state of two nucleons, while the antisymmetric function (3.7) corresponds to the $T = 0$, $T_3 = 0$ state of a neutron and a proton.

## The extended Pauli principle

A system of two identical fermions such as protons or neutrons, must, according to the Pauli principle, be described by an antisymmetrical complete wave function, $\chi$, that is, one that changes sign on interchange of the two particles. In symbols $\chi = \phi\alpha$ must be antisymmetric, where $\phi$ represents the spatial part of the wave function and $\alpha$ the ordinary spin component. Now $T = 1$ for two protons or two neutrons and the isotopic spin wave function (3.4) or (3.5) is symmetric. The total wave function $\chi = \phi\alpha\Psi$ is therefore still antisymmetric, where $\Psi$ represents one of the isotopic spin wave functions (3.4) to (3.7). This fact suggests an extended Pauli principle which states that the complete wave function $\phi\alpha\Psi$ *must* be antisymmetric.

The neutron–proton system can have $T = 1$ or $T = 0$, and $\phi\alpha$ can be either symmetric or antisymmetric, since the particles are not identical in this case. Thus in terms of the extended Pauli principle the $T = 0$ antisymmetric isotopic wave function (that is 3.7) will be associated with the symmetric $\phi\alpha$ wave function and the symmetric $T = 1$ (3.6) with the antisymmetric $\phi\alpha$. The former wave function has no counterpart in the *pp* or *nn* systems. The statement of charge independence is now that the nuclear interaction depends only on the total $T$ value of the state and not on the charges of the nucleons in this state; that is, the nuclear interaction does not depend on direction in the isotopic spin space, for charge is given by $T_3$, the component of $T$ in any specified direction in isotopic spin space.

The interaction is therefore a scalar quantity in this space. To summarize, conservation of $T_3$ in any reaction is simply charge conservation, while conservation of the total isotopic spin $T$ is a convenient representation of the hypothesis of charge independence. A fuller discussion of these points is given in the latter part of this chapter (p. 51).

The preceding remarks may be made clearer by the following tables, which are taken from the article by Burcham (1955). Table 4 gives the symmetries in the two-nucleon system. To illustrate the manner in which this table is derived, consider the first row. If the

TABLE 4

| Symmetry in | | | Spectroscopic classification | Interacting system |
|---|---|---|---|---|
| Space | Spin | Isotopic spin | | |
| $s$ | $s$ | $a$ | $^3S$ $^3D$ | $np$ |
| $s$ | $a$ | $s$ | $^1S$ $^1D$ ⎱ | $pp, nn, np$ |
| $a$ | $s$ | $s$ | $^3P$ $^3F$ ⎰ | |
| $a$ | $a$ | $a$ | $^1P$ $^1F$ | $np$ |

TABLE 5

| Spectroscopic classification | Interacting system | Total isotopic spin $T$ | $T_3$ |
|---|---|---|---|
| $^3S$ $^3D$ | $np$ | 0 | 0 |
| $^1S$ $^1D$ ⎰ | ⎧ $pp$ | 1 | 1 |
| | ⎨ $np$ | 1 | 0 |
| $^3P$ $^3F$ ⎰ | ⎩ $nn$ | 1 | −1 |
| $^1P$ $^1F$ | $np$ | 0 | 0 |

system is symmetrical in space and spin then by the Pauli principle it can only describe dissimilar nucleons. Thus the interacting system is an $np$ system. Further, if it is symmetrical in spin then the two spins are parallel so that $2S + 1 = 3$, while if it is symmetrical in space then $L$ must be even. Hence the spectroscopic classification is

$^3S$, $^3D$, etc. The system is antisymmetric in isotopic spin by the extended Pauli principle. The remaining rows of the table may be obtained in a similar manner. The possible states of the two-nucleon system are given in Table 5. It can be seen, from an examination of the last two columns, that for a given isotopic spin $T$, the multiplicity of the state is $2T + 1$.

## Isotopic spin and mesons

The discussion so far has considered only nucleons. The next problem is to assign an isotopic spin to the pion and to discuss its representation.

One of the basic assumptions of the Yukawa theory is that pions are emitted and absorbed by nucleons one at a time. In symbols

$$p \longrightarrow n + \pi^+ \qquad (3.8)$$

for example, is an important virtual reaction. If sufficient energy is available then (3.8) becomes a real reaction, as, for example, when a gamma-ray of more than 150 MeV kinetic energy strikes a proton. In such a case the two reactions

$$\left. \begin{array}{l} \gamma + p \longrightarrow p + \pi^0 \\ \gamma + p \longrightarrow n + \pi^+ \end{array} \right\} \qquad (3.9)$$

are observed.

In the dissociation process (3.8) $T_3 = -\frac{1}{2}$ for the neutron and $T_3 = +\frac{1}{2}$ for the proton, so that in order to conserve $T_3$, $T_3(\pi^+) = +1$. Similarly $T_3(\pi^-) = -1$ and $T_3(\pi^0) = 0$, as may readily be seen by writing down equations similar to (3.8), involving $\pi^-$- and $\pi^0$-mesons. This suggests that, for the pion, the total isotopic spin $T$ is unity, with three components $+1$, $0$ and $-1$, and that the charge of a pion is related to its isotopic spin component $T_3$ by the equation

$$Q = T_3 \qquad (3.10)$$

It is convenient now to introduce an isotopic spin operator, $\tau$, with three components, $\tau_1$, $\tau_2$ and $\tau_3$, which are formally identical with the Pauli spin matrices, and which operate on two-component wave functions such as (3.3). They are, therefore

$$\tau_1 = \begin{pmatrix} 0 & 1 \\ 1 & 0 \end{pmatrix}; \ \tau_2 = \begin{pmatrix} 0 & -i \\ i & 0 \end{pmatrix}; \ \tau_3 = \begin{pmatrix} 1 & 0 \\ 0 & -1 \end{pmatrix} \qquad (3.11)$$

Remembering that to multiply matrices one multiplies the first row and then the second row into the column of the two-component matrix, it may be shown that

$$\begin{aligned}\tfrac{1}{2}(\tau_1 + i\tau_2)u_n &= u_p \\ \text{and} \qquad \tfrac{1}{2}(\tau_1 - i\tau_2)u_p &= u_n \end{aligned} \Bigg\} \qquad (3.12)$$

In other words, $\tfrac{1}{2}(\tau_1 + i\tau_2)$ has the effect of changing a neutron to a proton, and $\tfrac{1}{2}(\tau_1 - i\tau_2)$ that of changing a proton to a neutron. Special notations are used for these operators, viz.

$$\begin{aligned}\tau_+ &= \tfrac{1}{2}(\tau_1 + i\tau_2) = \begin{pmatrix} 0 & 1 \\ 0 & 0 \end{pmatrix} \\ \text{and} \qquad \tau_- &= \tfrac{1}{2}(\tau_1 - i\tau_2) = \begin{pmatrix} 0 & 0 \\ 1 & 0 \end{pmatrix} \end{aligned} \Bigg\} \qquad (3.13)$$

If a neutron changes to a proton, or vice versa, clearly a charged pion must be produced in order to conserve charge. It is therefore necessary to have a symbolism to describe the different mesons in a convenient way. The convention adopted is to describe the pion field by a vector (in isotopic spin or charge space) $\boldsymbol{\phi}$, which has three components $\phi_1$, $\phi_2$, $\phi_3$, corresponding to the different charge states of the pion. The situation is slightly more complicated than this, for it turns out that the charged pions are described by linear combinations of $\phi_1$ and $\phi_2$, while $\phi_3$ represents directly the wave function of the $\pi^0$-meson. In fact

$$\phi_+ = \frac{1}{\sqrt{2}}\,(\phi_1 + i\phi_2) \quad \text{corresponding to } \pi^+\text{-meson}$$

$$\phi_- = \frac{1}{\sqrt{2}}\,(\phi_1 - i\phi_2) \quad \text{corresponding to } \pi^-\text{-meson}$$

$$\phi_0 = \phi_3 \qquad\qquad\qquad \text{corresponding to } \pi^0\text{-meson}$$

$$(3.14)$$

In this case the pion fields ($\phi_+$, $\phi_0$, $\phi_-$) correspond to the three components $T_3 = +1, 0, -1$ of a pion of isotopic spin 1. It is useful to draw the analogy with ordinary angular momentum for the case in which $l = 1$ and $m = +1, 0, -1$, $m$ being the components of $l$ in any specified direction. The angular momentum eigenfunctions are the spherical harmonics $Y_l^m(\theta, \varphi)$ which are proportional to

$P_l^m(\cos \theta)e^{im\varphi}$. For $l = 1$ and $m = +1, 0, -1$, these eigenfunctions are

$$Y_1^1 = \frac{1}{\sqrt{2}}\sin \theta \, e^{i\varphi}, \quad Y_1^0 = \cos \theta, \quad Y_1^{-1} = \frac{1}{\sqrt{2}} \sin \theta \, e^{-i\varphi}$$

Multiplying these by $r$ for convenience, the eigenfunctions have the following expressions in terms of $x, y, z$ coordinates:

$$m = +1 \text{ eigenfunction} = \frac{1}{\sqrt{2}} r \sin \theta \, e^{i\varphi} = \frac{1}{\sqrt{2}} (x + iy)$$

$$\text{cf. } \frac{1}{\sqrt{2}} (\phi_1 + i\phi_2)$$

$$m = 0 \quad ,, \quad = r \cos \theta \quad = z \quad \text{cf. } \phi_3$$

$$m = -1 \quad ,, \quad = \frac{1}{\sqrt{2}} r \sin \theta \, e^{-i\varphi} = \frac{1}{\sqrt{2}} (x - iy)$$

$$\text{cf. } \frac{1}{\sqrt{2}} (\phi_1 - i\phi_2)$$

In certain circumstances $\phi_+$, $\phi_-$ and $\phi_0$ may be regarded as operators which operate on the meson field variables, creating (or annihilating) a single pion if the state does not (or does) contain a pion. $\phi_+$ will create a positive pion or destroy a negative pion, $\phi_-$ will create a negative pion or destroy a positive pion, while $\phi_0$ will create or annihilate a neutral pion. An example of the use of the $\tau$ and $\phi$ operators is given in the next section. The mathematical representation of $\phi$ as an operator is discussed in Appendix I.

### Isotopic spin wave functions for the pion–nucleon system

Charge independence for the interaction between a pion and a nucleon was first proposed by Kemmer (1938). This provides a direct interpretation of the charge independence of nuclear forces. Therefore, the interaction of a pion and a nucleon, of definite total angular momentum $J$ and parity $\omega$, depends only on their total isotopic spin $T$, which may have the values $T = \frac{3}{2}$ or $T = \frac{1}{2}$. The possible values of $T_3$ are $\pm\frac{1}{2}$, $\pm\frac{3}{2}$ in the first case and $\pm\frac{1}{2}$ for the second case. In considering the interactions between pions and nucleons it is convenient to write down the various isotopic spin states, of $T$ and $T_3$, that are possible for the particular pion–nucleon system being studied. Conversely, for a given value of $T$ and $T_3$ it is possible to write down the various pion–nucleon combinations that contribute to this state.

The $\pi^+ + p$ system, for example, can only have $T = \frac{3}{2}$ since $T_3 = \frac{3}{2}$ in this case. However, the systems $\pi^- + p$ and $\pi^0 + n$, which have a total $T_3$ of $-\frac{1}{2}$, are mixtures of states of $T = \frac{3}{2}$ and $T = \frac{1}{2}$. We will now derive the different combinations of pion and nucleon which have definite values of total $T$ and total $T_3$; these combinations, or isotopic wave functions, will be denoted by $\Psi(T, T_3)$.

Clearly

$$\Psi(\tfrac{3}{2}, +\tfrac{3}{2}) = u_p \pi^+ \tag{3.15}$$

and similarly

$$\Psi(\tfrac{3}{2}, -\tfrac{3}{2}) = u_n \pi^- \tag{3.16}$$

for in this case $T_3 = -\frac{3}{2}$ which can only be obtained from a $T = \frac{3}{2}$ state.

The form of the states $\Psi(\tfrac{1}{2}, +\tfrac{1}{2})$ and $\Psi(\tfrac{1}{2}, -\tfrac{1}{2})$ may be derived as follows. The operator $\boldsymbol{\tau}.\boldsymbol{\phi}$, acting on a nucleon state, gives rise to a pion–nucleon state; $\boldsymbol{\tau}$ may, or may not, change the charge of the nucleon, while $\boldsymbol{\phi}$ operates on the meson field variables to create a pion such that charge is conserved. Since $\boldsymbol{\tau}.\boldsymbol{\phi}$ is a scalar quantity in isotopic spin space it cannot change the total isotopic spin $T$, or the component $T_3$, from their values for the initial nucleon state. The pion–nucleon state generated in this way therefore must have $T = \frac{1}{2}$ and $T_3 = +\frac{1}{2}, -\frac{1}{2}$, according as the initial nucleon state is a proton or a neutron state.

The operator $\boldsymbol{\tau}.\boldsymbol{\phi}$ will now be written in terms of the components of the pion field. Thus

$$\boldsymbol{\tau}.\boldsymbol{\phi} = \tau_1 \phi_1 + \tau_2 \phi_2 + \tau_3 \varphi_3$$
$$= \tau_1 \frac{1}{\sqrt{2}}(\phi_+ + \phi_-) + \tau_2 \frac{1}{\sqrt{2}}\cdot\frac{1}{i}(\phi_+ - \phi_-) + \tau_3 \varphi_3$$

$$\therefore \ \boldsymbol{\tau}.\boldsymbol{\phi} = \sqrt{2}\,\tau_- \phi_+ + \sqrt{2}\,\tau_+ \phi_- + \tau_3 \phi_0 \tag{3.17}$$

If this expression operates on a proton wave function $u_p$, the first term changes the proton to a neutron ($\tau_-$) while $\phi_+$ yields a positive meson; the second term is zero by (3.3) and (3.13); the third term

PLATE I

A photograph of experimental equipment outside the shielding wall (on the left) of the 660 MeV synchro-cyclotron at the Dubna Institute, U.S.S.R. Proton beams pass through the counter telescopes in the foreground, positive pion and neutron beams are in the centre of the room, and the negative pion beams are on the far side

(By courtesy of Professor M. G. Mescheryakov)

PLATE II

$p$

$\pi^-$

$\pi^-$

An example of the elastic scattering of a 867 MeV negative pion by a proton, observed in a 10″ diameter liquid hydrogen bubble chamber at Berkeley, California. A magnetic field was applied across the chamber, and the opposite curvatures of the pion and proton can be seen

(Photograph by courtesy of Professor L. W. Alvarez)

PLATE III

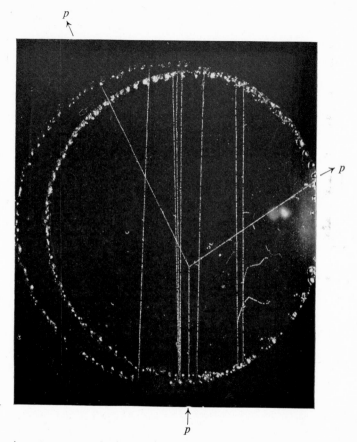

A proton–proton elastic scattering event observed in a 6″ liquid
hydrogen bubble chamber at Carnegie Institute of Technology.
The energy of the incident proton beam was 450 MeV

(By courtesy of Professor T. H. Fields)

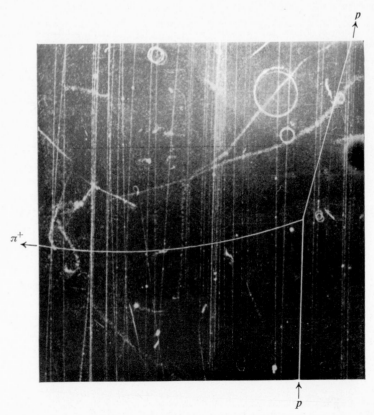

A proton–proton collision, in an 18″ hydrogen-filled diffusion chamber, which gives rise to a positive pion, a proton and a neutron. A magnetic field of 13 kgauss was applied across the chamber; the hydrogen was at a pressure of 24 atmospheres. (It has been necessary to retouch the three tracks of interest)

(Photograph by courtesy of Dr A. P. Batson and Dr L. Riddiford) leaves the proton unchanged but can yield a neutral meson. In symbols

$$(\tau \cdot \phi)u_p = \sqrt{2}u_n\pi^+ + u_p\pi^0$$

To obtain $\Psi(\frac{1}{2}, +\frac{1}{2})$ we must normalize this expression, that is

$$\int |\Psi(\tfrac{1}{2}, +\tfrac{1}{2})|^2 \, dv = 1 \text{ where } \int |u_n\pi^+|^2 \, dv = \int |u_p\pi^0|^2 \, dv = 1$$

so that we must divide by $\sqrt{3}$. Therefore

$$\Psi(\tfrac{1}{2}, +\tfrac{1}{2}) = \sqrt{\tfrac{2}{3}}u_n\pi^+ + \sqrt{\tfrac{1}{3}}u_p\pi^0 \tag{3.18}$$

and similarly

$$\Psi(\tfrac{1}{2}, -\tfrac{1}{2}) = \sqrt{\tfrac{2}{3}}u_p\pi^- - \sqrt{\tfrac{1}{3}}u_n\pi^0 \tag{3.19}$$

To obtain $\Psi(\frac{3}{2}, +\frac{1}{2})$ we make use of the fact that this wave function and that for $\Psi(\frac{1}{2}, +\frac{1}{2})$ must be orthogonal. This follows by analogy with the theory of ordinary spin.* Therefore

$$\Psi(\tfrac{3}{2}, +\tfrac{1}{2}) = \sqrt{\tfrac{2}{3}}u_p\pi^0 - \sqrt{\tfrac{1}{3}}u_n\pi^+ \tag{3.20}$$

and similarly

$$\Psi(\tfrac{3}{2}, -\tfrac{1}{2}) = \sqrt{\tfrac{1}{3}}u_p\pi^- + \sqrt{\tfrac{2}{3}}u_n\pi^0 \tag{3.21}$$

It should be noted that some authors have used a sign convention which is different to that adopted here.

We may rearrange the expressions for $\Psi(T, T_3)$ and express a given pion nucleon system in terms of the isotopic spin states. For a pion and a proton it is readily shown that

$$u_p\pi^+ = \Psi(\tfrac{3}{2}, +\tfrac{3}{2}) \tag{3.22}$$

$$u_p\pi^- = \sqrt{\tfrac{1}{3}}\Psi(\tfrac{3}{2}, -\tfrac{1}{2}) + \sqrt{\tfrac{2}{3}}\Psi(\tfrac{1}{2}, -\tfrac{1}{2}) \tag{3.23}$$

$$u_p\pi^0 = \sqrt{\tfrac{2}{3}}\Psi(\tfrac{3}{2}, +\tfrac{1}{2}) + \sqrt{\tfrac{1}{3}}\Psi(\tfrac{1}{2}, +\tfrac{1}{2}) \tag{3.24}$$

### Elastic scattering of particles by a centre of force

In order to obtain information about the forces acting between particles, a fruitful mode of attack on the problem is to scatter the particles one on the other, and to observe the energy and angular distributions of the scattered particles. For analysis it is usual to represent the target particle (which may be a single nucleon or a complex nucleus) by a small spherically symmetric region in which

* Schiff, *Quantum Mechanics*, 2nd Ed., pp. 43–5, 233.

the incident particles have a potential energy $V(r)$ different from zero. This potential thus describes the force that is acting and the problem is to relate the measured quantities to this potential. One way of doing this is to employ the partial wave analysis which we now describe, following the approach of Mott and Massey (1949). We will consider only the case of the elastic scattering of non-identical particles.

The incident beam of particles moving with velocity $v$ and momentum $p$ along the $z$ axis from left to right, may be represented by a plane wave $e^{ikz}$* where $k = p/\hbar$. This wave will be scattered by the centre of force and the amplitude of the scattered wave at any point $(r, \theta, \phi)$ may be written as $f(\theta)e^{ikr}/r$ where $\theta$ is measured with respect to the $z$ axis. A factor $1/r$ appears, for the radial flux must fall off as the inverse square of the distance; the function $f(\theta)$ is to be determined.

The probability of finding a particle in the scattered beam at a point $(r, \theta, \phi)$ is $|f(\theta)|^2/r^2$, and crossing an area $dS = r^2\,d\omega$ is $\dfrac{|f(\theta)|^2}{r^2}$ $r^2\,d\omega$ where $d\omega$ is the solid angle subtended by $dS$ at the scattering centre. The number of particles crossing the area $dS$ per unit time will be

$$v \cdot \frac{|f(\theta)|^2}{r^2} \cdot r^2\,d\omega \tag{3.25}$$

Suppose that we take unit particle density in the incoming beam; the flux = no. per unit volume × velocity = $v$. The quantity that is observed in any scattering experiment is the number of particles scattered into unit solid angle, per unit time, per unit flux. This is known as the differential cross-section, and from (3.25) it is equal to $|f(\theta)|^2$.

The problem, therefore, is to find a solution of the wave equation which, at a large distance from the scattering centre, represents an incident wave and a scattered wave. That is, for large $r$

$$\psi \sim e^{ikz} + \frac{e^{ikr}f(\theta)}{r} \tag{3.26}$$

* Strictly speaking this should be multiplied by a time factor, $e^{-iE_k t}$ where $E_k$ is the total energy of the incident particle.

The Schrödinger equation for a particle in a spherically symmetric potential $V(r)$ may be written as

$$\nabla^2 \psi + [k^2 - U(r)]\psi = 0 \quad \text{where} \quad U(r) = \frac{8\pi^2 m}{h^2} V(r) \tag{3.27}$$

The most general solution of this equation, is

$$\psi = \sum_{l=0}^{\infty} \frac{A_l}{r} f_l(r) P_l(\cos \theta) \tag{3.28}$$

where the radial wave function $f_l(r)$ must have the form

$$(-e^{-i(kr - l\pi/2)} + S_l e^{i(kr - l\pi/2)}) \tag{3.29}$$

for large $r$ such that the interaction $U(r)$ is negligible. The first term of (3.29) represents an *incoming* spherical wave and the second term an *outgoing* spherical wave. The constant $A_l$ is to be determined. If the scattering is entirely elastic then $|S_l|^2$ must equal unity for each $l$, since the total outward flux must then equal the ingoing flux for each angular momentum wave. In this case $S_l$ may be written $e^{2i\delta_l}$, where $\delta_l$ is called the phase shift and is a real quantity; physically it represents half the difference in phase between the outgoing scattered wave and the ingoing wave. If there is no potential, and therefore no scattering, then $S_l = 1$ and $\delta_l = 0$, the phase shift is zero.

We must now identify (3.26) with (3.28) and (3.29); we first note that for large $r$ we can write*

$$e^{ikz} = e^{ikr \cos \theta} = \sum_l \frac{1}{kr} (2l + 1) i^l P_l(\cos \theta) \sin (kr - l\pi/2) \tag{3.30}$$

Then

$$\sum_l \frac{A_l}{r} (-e^{-i(kr-l\pi/2)} + S_l e^{i(kr-l\pi/2)} P_l(\cos \theta)$$

$$= \sum_l \frac{(2l + 1) i^l}{2ikr} (e^{i(kr-l\pi/2)} - e^{-i(kr-l\pi/2)}) P_l(\cos \theta) + \frac{f(\theta) e^{ikr}}{r} \tag{3.31}$$

By comparing the terms in $e^{-ikr}$ we have at once that

$$A_l = \frac{(2l + 1) i^l}{2ik} \tag{3.32}$$

* Proved in Mott and Massey, *Theory of Atomic Collisions*, pp. 20-2. O.U.P.

Equating the coefficients of $e^{+ikr}$ on either side of (3.31)

$$f(\theta) = \sum_l \frac{(2l + 1)}{2ik} P_l(\cos \theta) \{e^{2i\delta_l} - 1\}$$

or $$f(\theta) = \sum_l \frac{(2l + 1)}{k} P_l(\cos \theta) e^{i\delta_l} \sin \delta_l \qquad (3.33)$$

We have already shown that the differential cross-section, usually written as $d\sigma/d\omega$, is equal to $|f(\theta)|^2$. Thus the total cross-section, $\sigma$, is given by

$$\sigma = \int \frac{d\sigma}{d\omega} . d\omega = \int |f(\theta)|^2 \sin \theta \, d\theta \, d\phi$$

Taking into account the orthogonality relations for the Legendre polynomials, namely

$$\int_0^\pi P_l(\cos \theta) P_{l'}(\cos \theta) \sin \theta \, d\theta = 0 \quad \text{for } l \neq l'$$

and

$$\int_0^\pi P_l^2(\cos \theta) \sin \theta \, d\theta = \frac{2}{2l + 1}$$

then this integration over the differential cross-section leads to the result

$$\sigma = \frac{4\pi}{k^2} \sum_l (2l + 1) \sin^2 \delta_l$$

$$= 4\pi \lambda^2 \sum_l (2l + 1) \sin^2 \delta_l \qquad (3.34)$$

since $\lambda = \hbar/p = 1/k$

The method of this section is for the scattering of non-identical particles. We have also neglected the spins of the scattering particles, so that the theory given will not be valid if spin-orbit forces are present.

In (3.34) since $\sin \delta_l \leqslant 1$, the cross-section for each partial wave cannot exceed $4\pi\lambda^2(2l + 1)$, for the appropriate $l$. Also if the scattering centre is confined to a region of radius $a$, the number of partial waves effective in scattering is limited. This limit can be obtained from a simple classical argument. Let scattering occur when the impact parameter '$b$' is less than '$a$'. The angular momentum of the incoming particle will be $pb = \hbar k b = L = l\hbar$ (say). Therefore $b = l/k$ and we assume that scattering takes place if $b \leqslant a$, i.e. if $l \leqslant ka = pa/\hbar$. It is usual to put '$a$' equal to the Compton wavelength of the pi-meson $= \hbar/m_\pi c \sim 10^{-13}$ cm, since this is the characteristic range of nuclear forces, and then $l$ can be calculated as a function of the momentum (in the centre-of-mass system) of the incident particle. For nucleon–nucleon scattering $l_{max} = 1$ when the incident particle has about 20 MeV kinetic energy in the laboratory system; for pion–nucleon scattering the corresponding pion energy for $l_{max} = 1$ is around 140 MeV. Thus it is at energies of this order of magnitude that the partial wave analysis is of particular value, although it can be used at higher energies by taking into account more $l$ values. The representation of the data in terms of phase shifts forms a convenient intermediate step between the raw data of angular distributions, and total cross-sections, and the scattering potential $U$, and enables us to focus attention on the dominant scattering waves and their characteristics. The ultimate problem is to understand the nature and origin of the potential $U$ which gives rise to the observed scattering phase shifts.

A particularly useful relation exists between the scattering amplitude for $\theta = 0$, known as the forward scattering amplitude, and the total elastic cross-section. For $\theta = 0$, (3.33) may be written as

$$f(0) = \sum_l \frac{(2l + 1)}{k} [\sin \delta_l \cos \delta_l + i \sin^2 \delta_l]$$

so that

$$Im\, f(0) = \sum \frac{(2l + 1)}{k} \sin^2 \delta_l$$

This expression may be substituted in (3.34), yielding

$$\sigma \text{ (total elastic)} = \frac{4\pi}{k} Im\, f(0) \tag{3.35a}$$

In fact, (3.35a) is a special case of a more general relation, known as the Optical Theorem, which is valid when both elastic scattering and absorption occur. It has the same form as (3.35*a*), but the cross-section in question is then the total cross-section, viz.

$$\sigma(\text{total}) = \sigma(\text{elastic}) + \sigma(\text{absorption}) = \frac{4\pi}{k} Im f(0) \quad (3.35b)$$

A simple derivation of (3.35*b*) is given in Chapter VI, p. 110.

*Some characteristic angular distributions*

For *S* wave scattering $l = 0$ and from (3.33)

$$f(\theta) = \frac{1}{k} e^{i\delta_0} \sin \delta_0 \quad \text{and} \quad \frac{d\sigma}{d\omega} = \frac{\sin^2 \delta_0}{k^2} \quad (3.36)$$

For *P* waves only $l = 1$, thus $P_1(\cos \theta) = \cos \theta$ and

$$f(\theta) = \frac{3}{k} \cos \theta \; e^{i\delta_1} \sin \delta_1$$

$$\frac{d\sigma}{d\omega} = \frac{9}{k^2} \cos^2 \theta \sin^2 \delta_1 \quad (3.37)$$

For *S* and *P* waves

$$\frac{d\sigma}{d\omega} = |f(\theta)|^2 = \frac{1}{k^2} | e^{i\delta_0} \sin \delta_0 + 3e^{i\delta_1} \sin \delta_1 \cos \theta |^2$$

$$= \frac{1}{k^2}[\sin^2 \delta_0 + 6 \sin \delta_0 \sin \delta_1 \cos (\delta_1 - \delta_0) \cos \theta$$

$$+ 9 \sin^2 \delta_1 \cos^2 \theta] \quad (3.38)$$

A term in $\cos \theta$, which gives rise to a forward-to-backward asymmetry in the angular distribution, can only arise from interference between *S* and *P* waves or, more generally, from interference between even and odd waves.

## The quantum mechanical description of pions and nucleons

*Introduction*

The description of the interaction between pion and nucleon has been developed by analogy with the interaction of the electromagnetic field with charged particles, and for a proper appreciation requires some knowledge of the quantum theory of fields. A necessarily brief review of this subject will be given here; a more complete introduction can be found in the articles by Peierls *et al.* (1955) or in the standard texts such as those by Dirac and by Schiff. [See also McConnell, 1958.]

Consider first the equations of motion of an electromagnetic field in the absence of charges. These are the wave equations for the electric field $\mathbf{E}$ and the magnetic field $\mathbf{H}$

$$\left(\nabla^2 - \frac{1}{c^2}\frac{\partial^2}{\partial t^2}\right)\mathbf{E} = 0$$

and
$$\left(\nabla^2 - \frac{1}{c^2}\frac{\partial^2}{\partial t^2}\right)\mathbf{H} = 0$$

To come closer to meson theory, it is better to consider $\mathbf{E}$ and $\mathbf{H}$ derived from a potential which has four components, the scalar potential $V$, and the three components of the vector potential $\mathbf{A}$. In terms of these

$$\mathbf{E} = \nabla V - \frac{1}{c}\frac{\partial \mathbf{A}}{\partial t}$$

and $\mathbf{H} = \text{curl } \mathbf{A}$.

It is convenient to use the relativistic notation of writing $V = A_4$, and to use the symbol $A_\mu$ for the four components of $\mathbf{A}$, where $\mu = 1, 2, 3$ for the vector potential and 4 for the scalar potential. It may readily be shown that $A_\mu$ satisfies

$$\left(\nabla^2 - \frac{1}{c^2}\frac{\partial^2}{\partial t^2}\right)A_\mu = 0 \tag{3.39a}$$

Now consider the introduction of charged particles. For a static charge distribution $\rho$, one has the familiar equation that

$$\nabla . \mathbf{E} = 4\pi\rho$$
or
$$\nabla^2 V = -4\pi\rho$$

and for a current distribution $\mathbf{j}$

$$\nabla^2 \mathbf{A} = -4\pi\mathbf{j}$$

These can be combined to give the general time dependent form which is the generalization of the equations for $\mathbf{E}$ and $\mathbf{H}$, i.e.

$$\left.\begin{aligned}\left(\nabla^2 - \frac{1}{c^2}\frac{\partial^2}{\partial t^2}\right)V &= -4\pi\rho \\ \left(\nabla^2 - \frac{1}{c^2}\frac{\partial^2}{\partial t^2}\right)\mathbf{A} &= -4\pi\mathbf{j}\end{aligned}\right\} \tag{3.39b}$$

and

The potential from a static source is given by

$$V(\mathbf{r}) = \int \frac{\rho(\mathbf{r}')\, d^3\mathbf{r}'}{|\mathbf{r} - \mathbf{r}'|}$$

and the interaction energy between a particle of charge $e$ at $r_1$ with one at $r_2$ is just $e^2/r_{12}$.

For the interaction between two nucleons Yukawa introduced a new kind of field, described by a function $\phi$ such that, in the absence of sources, $\phi$ 'waves' satisfied a modification of the wave equation, viz.

$$\left\{\nabla^2 - \frac{1}{c^2}\frac{\partial^2}{\partial t^2} - \left(\frac{mc}{\hbar}\right)^2\right\}\phi = 0 \qquad (1.3)$$

This form of equation is a generalization of the wave equation $(3.39a)$ describing the electromagnetic field whose quanta are of zero mass, and is suggested by the energy-momentum relation

$$E^2 - p^2c^2 - m^2c^4 = 0$$

for a massive particle of mass $m$, as we have shown in Chapter I. A source term $4\pi\rho$ may next be written on the right-hand side of (1.3), in analogy with equations $(3.39b)$. For a static source $\rho(r)$ the $\phi$ field generated has the form

$$\phi(\mathbf{r}) = \int \rho(\mathbf{r}')\frac{\exp\left(-\dfrac{mc}{\hbar}|\mathbf{r} - \mathbf{r}'|\right)}{|\mathbf{r} - \mathbf{r}'|}d^3\mathbf{r}'$$

and the interaction energy between two point nucleon sources, each of strength $f$, will have the form

$$V(\mathbf{r}) = f^2 \exp\left(-\frac{mc}{\hbar}|\mathbf{r} - \mathbf{r}'|\right)\bigg/|\mathbf{r} - \mathbf{r}'|$$

corresponding to a potential of short range, $\sim \hbar/mc$.

Now just as the classical wave equation has electromagnetic waves as solutions, which in a quantized theory are described by assemblies of photons, so the Yukawa wave equation has solutions which in a quantized theory are described by assemblies of pions, which are Bose particles of mass $m$. In the quantized theory of the electromagnetic field, the Coulomb potential between two charged particles can be considered as arising from the transfer of virtual electromagnetic quanta (transverse and longitudinal photons) between the particles. In these terms the nucleon–nucleon force, due to the intermediate Yukawa field, can be regarded as due to the virtual transfer of pions, the massive quanta of the Yukawa field (see pp. 6–9). The way in which the pion field is quantized is discussed briefly in Appendix I, using the case of the harmonic oscillator as an example. It is sufficient here to say that in certain circumstances $\phi$, which has three components given by (3.14), may be regarded as an operator, which operates on the function specifying the pion state of a given system, and annihilates or creates pions as the case may be. The mathematical formulation of this property is given in Appendix I.

*The interaction energy between a nucleon and the meson field*

Let us now consider the interaction energy between a nucleon and the meson field. By analogy with the energy of a charged particle, $e$, at a position, $r$, in a field $V(r)$ which is just $e\,V(r)$, we expect an interaction energy $U(r) = f\,\phi(r)$ where the nucleon of strength $f$ is at position $r$. Now consider this expression from the point of view of quantum theory. The use of $\phi$ at the position of the nucleon, $r$, must be multiplied by the probability of finding a nucleon at $r$ which is $\bar{\psi}(r)\,\psi(r)$, where $\psi$ is the nucleon wave function. This gives $U = f\bar{\psi}(r)\psi(r)\phi(r)$ as an energy density.

In the same way that $\phi$ can be considered a quantized field variable (Appendix I), so we can think of the nucleon field and consider $\psi(r)$ as a quantized operator. Then $U$ can be interpreted as the energy from the annihilation of a nucleon and the creation of a nucleon and a meson. The interaction can be represented diagrammatically by a vertex with a line for $\bar{\psi}$, a line for $\psi$, joined at a junction with a dotted line for $\phi$, the junction being associated with the number $f$ (Fig. 2). This interaction produces mesons singly.

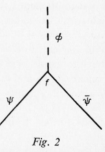

*Fig. 2*

To become more specific we need a more general form for $U$ to allow for the dependence of the interaction upon the charge, and spins, of the particles concerned. Consider the charge first. There are four possible interactions, namely $\bar{\psi}_p\psi_p\phi_0$; $\bar{\psi}_n\psi_n\phi_0$; $\bar{\psi}_n\psi_p\phi_-$; $\bar{\psi}_p\psi_n\phi_+$ corresponding to the fact that, say, $\pi^- + p \rightarrow n$ etc. If $\psi_p$, $\psi_n$ are written as a $2 \times 1$ matrix $\psi = \begin{pmatrix} \psi_p \\ \psi_n \end{pmatrix}$, and if we confine ourselves

E

to the symmetric meson theory introduced by Kemmer (1938), then the four interactions can be combined as

$$\bar{\psi}(g_1\tau_1\phi_1 + g_2\tau_2\phi_2 + g_3\tau_3\phi_3)\psi$$

where the $\tau_1$, $\tau_2$, $\tau_3$ are the $2 \times 2$ matrices defined in (3.11) and $\phi_1$, $\phi_2$ and $\phi_3$ are defined by (3.14). The coupling constant associated with positive pions ($\phi_+$) is $g_1 + g_2$, since $\phi_+$ occurs in the expressions for $\phi_1$ and $\phi_2$ and similarly for $\phi_-$, while $\phi_0$ only involves $g_3$. In the symmetric theory $g_1 = g_2 = g_3 = f$ in our terminology, so that we can write

$$U \sim f(\bar{\psi}\, \mathbf{\tau}.\, \boldsymbol{\phi}\, \psi)$$

The mathematical symmetry of this form of the theory is borne out by its physically symmetric consequences. For example, if an equal mixture of protons and neutrons is scattered off a target of a similar mixture, then equal numbers of positive, negative and neutral mesons should be produced; this prediction is well borne out by the experimental data.

The last parameter which we must introduce is the spin of the nucleon. In the same way as we considered $\psi_p$, $\psi_n$ together as a $2 \times 1$ vector, the usual quantum mechanical treatment of spin uses a two-component $\psi$ for spin up and spin down for both proton and neutron. Altogether, therefore, the 'nucleon' is described by a four-component function. The observed spin dependence of the pion–nucleon interaction (see for example pp. 63 et seq.) suggests that the meson is coupled to ($\bar{\psi}\sigma\psi$) where $\sigma$ is the spin, with components $\sigma_x$, $\sigma_y$ and $\sigma_z$ given by the Pauli spin matrices. Now ($\bar{\psi}\sigma\psi$) is a vector quantity while the interaction energy is necessarily a scalar quantity. It is therefore necessary to combine this with a vector formed from $\phi$, and the only available vector is grad $\phi$. [Remember that $\phi$ is a pseudo-scalar in ordinary space; $\tau$ and $\boldsymbol{\phi}$ are vectors in isotopic spin space.] The final form for $U$ is then

$$U = f\bar{\psi}(\sigma.\nabla.\tau.\boldsymbol{\phi})\psi \qquad (3.40)$$

This has generally been referred to as pseudo-vector coupling (PV), because it involves the pseudo-vector $\sigma$ for the nucleons. It is effective only for $p$-wave mesons, for it involves $\nabla\phi$ at the origin, which is non-zero only for $p$-waves. This property follows directly from the basic assumption, made by Yukawa, that pions are emitted and absorbed singly. Now in the virtual reaction nucleon $\rightarrow$ nucleon + pion, parity can be conserved only when the meson has orbital angular momentum of unity for the pion has negative intrinsic parity and zero spin. The wave function for $l = 1$ vanishes at the origin, but the gradient of the field is finite.

The charge independence of the interaction, expressed by $\tau.\phi$, has been introduced to conform with the observed symmetry between the various pion–nucleon interactions. It can be viewed in a more general way by considering the three pion functions $\phi_1$, $\phi_2$, $\phi_3$, as components of a vector in 'isotopic' space. The nucleon, as we have seen, can be viewed as a spinor in this space, isotopic spin up being the proton and down the neutron. A vector constructed from the isotopic spin wave functions can only be $\bar{\psi}\tau\psi$. The interaction (3.40) is then invariant under rotations in this isotopic space, and leads to the concept of total isotopic spin $T$ and of the third component, $T_3$, being conserved quantities. Conservation of $T_3$ is equivalent to charge conservation, since the number of nucleons is conserved, and conservation of $T$ is equivalent to the charge symmetry which we need to build into the theory. The analogy is that of conservation of total angular momentum $\mathbf{J}$ in ordinary space, which is a good quantum number when the interaction between the spin $\sigma$ and the orbital angular momentum $\mathbf{L}$ is a scalar ($\sigma.\mathbf{L}$), even though $\sigma$ and $\mathbf{L}$ separately need not be conserved in any change of the system that they describe. Thus writing $\tau.\phi$ in the expression for the interaction energy implies that the interaction in a given state of nucleons and pions depends only on the total given isotopic spin value and not on the charges of the individual particles of the state. For example, the $^1S$ states of the $nn$, $np$ and $pp$ systems all correspond to $T = 1$, although they are of different charge (and therefore of different $T_3$). The rotational invariance of the basic interactions in isotopic spin space then requires that the interactions in these three systems be equal in the $^1S$ state, and this is known experimentally to be the case to a high degree of accuracy.

The interaction (3.40) still has a serious difficulty when used in theoretical calculations, as it leads to divergent results. A realistic calculation of pion–nucleon scattering involves estimations of the excitation of a cloud of virtual pions associated with a nucleon, and this involves the same kind of difficulty as the classical problem of the self energy of the electron. The field generated by an electron at $r_1$ at a point $r_2$ is $e^2/r_{12}$. But the electron itself is at the point $r_1$ and therefore has an interaction with itself of $e^2/0$, i.e. infinity. For the nucleon with a $\sigma.\nabla$ coupling this difficulty is made worse because the self energy is now $\left\{ \sigma\nabla.\sigma\nabla\dfrac{1}{r} \right\}_{r=0}$ which is 'more infinite', and this difficulty persists in scattering theory in a manner which is quite intractable. To overcome this difficulty the same device is used as in classical electron theory, that of giving the nucleon a size, that is, a distribution in space characterized by a source function $\rho$. The interaction then becomes

$$U = \frac{f}{m_\pi c^2} \int \bar{\psi}(x) \, \sigma.(\tau\nabla.\phi(y))\psi(x)\rho(x-y) \, d^3x d^3y \qquad (3.41)$$

where the nucleon is at $x$ and the meson at $y$; the mass of the pion, $m_\pi c^2$, is introduced so that $f$ then has the dimensions of an electric charge (cf. Chapter I). This device is non-relativistic and not easily generalized, but it can be regarded as giving a rough non-relativistic version of relativistic pseudo-scalar theory, the form function $\rho$ representing (approximately) the effect of recoil of the nucleon due to the virtual emission and absorption of pions. The adjustable parameters are the radius of the source and the pseudo-vector coupling constant $f$. The latter must be determined by experiment. The above discussion is a non-relativistic phenomenological derivation for the interaction energy, which assumes the nucleon to be stationary. Equation (3.41) may be regarded as a rough approximation to the complete pseudo-vector interaction (PV); it is valuable for orientation owing to its simplicity. This fixed-source theory was developed to a great extent by Chew (1954) (see also Chew and Low, 1956) at an early stage, but its successes in accounting for the data on pion scattering and photoproduction can now be paralleled and extended by the relativistic dispersion theory (cf. Chew, 1958).

As pointed out earlier, the fixed-source theory ignores mesons in $s$-states and can only hope to describe mesons in $p$-states. Thus it might be expected that this theory would be particularly applicable when $p$-wave mesons play a dominant part in an interaction.

The fully relativistic theory of the nucleon requires even more components than we have specified so far in order to describe the anti-particles. For example, the proton is described by four components corresponding to the four degrees of freedom of proton spin up, anti-proton spin up and the two spin downs. This allows us to generalize the interaction (3.40) in two different ways. The first way is one in which this interaction, roughly speaking, is the same for particles and anti-particles, without serious coupling between them, and in which the $\sigma$, a $2 \times 2$ matrix, is replaced by $\gamma_5 \gamma_\mu$ (see Peierls *et al.*, pp. 438, 451) which is a $4 \times 4$ matrix whose components are $\begin{pmatrix} \sigma & 0 \\ 0 & \sigma \end{pmatrix}$ for $\mu = 1, 2, 3$; $\begin{pmatrix} 0 & 1 \\ -1 & 0 \end{pmatrix}$ for 4 and $\begin{pmatrix} 0 & 1 \\ 1 & 0 \end{pmatrix}$ for $\gamma_5$. The second approach is rather more subtle and involves a coupling between proton and anti-proton, etc., via the term $G\bar{\psi}\gamma_5\psi(\boldsymbol{\tau}.\boldsymbol{\phi})$, where $G$ is the pseudo-scalar coupling constant. It is related to $f/m_\pi$ by

$$f/m_\pi = G/2M$$

where $M$ is the nucleon mass. $G$ is larger than $f/m_\pi$ by a factor involving the nucleon mass, due to the inclusion in the theory of nucleons and anti-nucleons, which are ignored in the non-relativistic pseudo-vector theory. It can be shown that this expression has the non-relativistic limit

$$\frac{G}{M}\bar{\psi}(\boldsymbol{\sigma}.\nabla)\psi(\boldsymbol{\tau}.\boldsymbol{\phi}) + \frac{G^2}{M}\bar{\psi}\psi\phi^2$$

The non-relativistic limits of both these interactions give the $p$-wave form (3.41). The pseudo-scalar interaction adds the term $\phi^2$, which corresponds to $s$-wave scattering of the pion; however, this does not agree with experiment since it predicts the same sign for both the S-wave scattering phase shifts, $\delta_1$ and $\delta_3$ (see p. 70). The PS interaction does, however, predict a very strong annihilation cross-section for nucleon–anti-nucleon scattering, as indeed is observed.

The essence of the present situation is that the simple $(\boldsymbol{\sigma}.\nabla)\boldsymbol{\tau}.\boldsymbol{\phi}$ coupling is very useful, but that the ultimate relativistic theory from which it stems is still obscure. The relativistic theories which have been considered all suffer from serious difficulties owing to the appearance of infinities which have not been mentioned here. This has led to a great interest in dispersion theory, which is mentioned in Chapter IV (p. 82), which, within certain limits, circumvents many of these troubles.

*Interactions between fields*

In the discussion of the photoproduction of pions, it will be necessary to consider the interaction between the electromagnetic field and the nucleon and pion fields. Consider first the pion field; we know that $\phi$ satisfies the equation

$$\left\{\nabla^2 - \frac{1}{c^2}\frac{\partial^2}{\partial t^2} - \frac{m^2c^2}{\hbar^2}\right\}\phi = 0 \tag{1.3}$$

or

$$\left\{\Box^2 - \frac{m^2c^2}{\hbar^2}\right\}\phi = 0$$

To introduce the electromagnetic field, described by $A_\mu(x)$ the rule is to replace $\Box$ by $\Box - ie\mathbf{A}$; this is required by gauge invariance for the electromagnetic field. This substitution yields

$$\left\{\Box^2 - ie2\mathbf{A}\Box - e^2\mathbf{A}^2 - \frac{m^2c^2}{\hbar^2}\right\}\phi = 0$$

and it can be shown that the two extra terms result from an interaction of the form $e\phi A_\mu\partial_\mu\phi + e^2 A_\mu{}^2\phi^2$, where $\partial_\mu = \left(\dfrac{\partial}{\partial x}, \dfrac{\partial}{\partial y}, \dfrac{\partial}{\partial z}, ic\dfrac{\partial}{\partial t}\right)$.

Consider next the nucleon and pion fields. It has been mentioned in the previous section that the non-relativistic limit of pseudo-scalar meson theory yields an expression for the interaction energy between a nucleon and the surrounding meson field of the form

$$U = \frac{f}{m_\pi c^2}\int \bar{\psi}(x)\boldsymbol{\sigma}.\nabla(\boldsymbol{\tau}.\boldsymbol{\phi}(y))\psi(x)\rho(x - y)d^3x\,d^3y \tag{3.41}$$

To introduce the e.m. field, this equation must be modified to include the vector potential $\mathbf{A}$ of the field. In fact it turns out that $\nabla\phi_\pm$ must be replaced by $\left(\nabla \mp \dfrac{ie}{c}\mathbf{A}\right)\phi_\pm$; $\nabla\phi_0$ remains unchanged, for there is no interaction between a neutral pion and an electromagnetic field. The *extra* contribution, $U'$, to the interaction energy arising from this term is thus

$$U' = \frac{f}{m_\pi c^2}.\frac{ie}{c}\int \boldsymbol{\sigma}.\mathbf{A}(-\sqrt{2}\tau_-\phi_+ + \sqrt{2}\tau_+\phi_-)\bar{\psi}\rho(r)\,d^3r\psi \tag{3.42}$$

where $\boldsymbol{\tau}.\boldsymbol{\phi}$ has been expanded using (3.17).

It is convenient to *visualize* the different interactions that we have discussed by means of simple diagrams. In these, initial and final particles are represented by lines leaving the diagram, full lines for nucleons, dotted lines for mesons and wavy lines for photons. Then, to catalogue the interaction, these incoming and outgoing lines are joined by vertices, an example of which has already been given in the discussion on meson–nucleon interactions. At these points the lines join according to the interaction in question and there is one

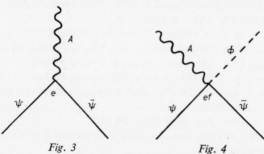

*Fig. 3*                    *Fig. 4*

line for each field function. The importance of each diagram can be gauged by the attachment of the appropriate coupling constant to each vertex. For example, the ordinary electromagnetic interaction of a proton with a photon has the vertex shown in Fig. 3, while the interaction $ef\bar{\psi}\sigma.\mathbf{A}(\tau_+\phi_- - \tau_-\phi_+)\psi$ has the vertex of Fig. 4. It may be remarked that these diagrams, which in this book are used solely as simple pictures of the interaction, can represent the quantitative values of the interaction by considering the lines and vertices as representations of functions which give the perturbation solution for the scattering. When used in this way they are known as Feynman diagrams.

## BIBLIOGRAPHY

BETHE, H. A. and DE HOFFMANN, F. 1955. *Mesons and Fields*, **II**. *Mesons*. Sections 30, 31. Row Peterson.

BURCHAM, W. E. 1955. *Progress in Nuclear Physics*, **4**, 171.

FERMI, E. 1955. *Nuovo Cimento*, **II**, Supplemento No. 1 (Varenna lectures), 17–31.

PEIERLS, R. E., SALAM, A., MATTHEWS, P. T. and FELDMAN, G. 1955. *Reports on Progress in Physics*, **18**, 423.

### Partial wave analysis

MOTT, N. F. and MASSEY, H. S. W. 1949. *The Theory of Atomic Collisions*. 2nd Ed. Ch. II. O.U.P.

### Elementary meson theory

BETHE, H. A. and MORRISON, P. 1956. *Elementary Nuclear Theory*. 2nd Ed. Ch. XVIII. Chapman & Hall.

DALITZ, R. H. 1955. *Progress in Nuclear Physics*, **4**, 95.

FERMI, E. 1950. *Nuclear Physics*. Ch. VII. University of Chicago Press; 1951. *Elementary Particles*. Oxford University Press.

HAMILTON, J. 1959. *The Theory of Elementary Particles*. O.U.P.

JACKSON, J. D. 1958. *The Physics of Elementary Particles*. Princeton University Press.

LOW, F. E. 1957. *Rev. Mod. Phys.* **29**, 216.

MCCONNELL, J. 1958. *Quantum Particle Dynamics*. Ch. XI and XII. North-Holland.

PEIERLS, R. E. *et al.* 1955. see above.

## REFERENCES

BREIT, G. and FEENBERG, E. 1936. *Phys. Rev.* **50**, 850.

CASSEN, B. and CONDON, E. U. 1936. *Phys. Rev.* **50**, 846.

CHEW, G. F. 1954. *Phys. Rev.* **95**, 1669; 1958. *Handbuch der Physik* **43**. Springer.

CHEW, G. F. and LOW, F. E. 1956. *Phys. Rev.* **101**, 1570, 1579.

KEMMER, N. 1938. *Proc. Roy. Soc.* **A166**, 127; *Proc. Camb. Phil. Soc.* **34**, 354.

# CHAPTER IV

# The Scattering of Pions by Protons

In order to study in detail the interactions of pions with matter it is necessary to have available beams of mono-energetic pions. There are now many synchro-cyclotrons, mostly in the United States (see Table 1), that can supply intense pion beams of energy up to about 220 MeV. The large synchro-cyclotrons at Berkeley, CERN and Dubna yield pions with energies up to about 400 MeV. Higher energy pion beams, but of much lower intensity, are obtained from the proton synchrotrons.

The most important interaction that has been studied is the scattering of charged pions by protons, in the form of hydrogen. The elastic scattering processes are

$$\pi^+ + p \longrightarrow \pi^+ + p \qquad (4.1)$$
$$\pi^- + p \longrightarrow \pi^- + p \qquad (4.2)$$
$$\pi^- + p \longrightarrow \pi^0 + n \qquad (4.3)$$

The total cross-sections for these processes will be written as $\sigma_T{}^+$, $\sigma_T{}^-$ and $\sigma_T{}^0$ respectively. We shall not consider those reactions which lead to the creation of pions. In terms of isotopic spin states, using the nomenclature of Chapter III, we can write that in reaction (4.1) an initial proton and positive pion state $(u_p\pi^+)$ transforms to a final $u_p\pi^+$ state with a scattering amplitude appropriate to the $T = \frac{3}{2}$ state, which can be written as $a(\frac{3}{2})$. Reactions (4.2) and (4.3) involve the scattering amplitude for the $T = \frac{1}{2}$ state, $a(\frac{1}{2})$ as well as $a(\frac{3}{2})$, for the initial $u_p\pi^-$ state is

$$u_p\pi^- = \sqrt{\tfrac{1}{3}}\, \Psi(\tfrac{3}{2}, -\tfrac{1}{2}) + \sqrt{\tfrac{2}{3}}\, \Psi(\tfrac{1}{2}, -\tfrac{1}{3}) \quad \text{(from 3.23)}$$

The scattering amplitude for the final states of (4.2) and (4.3) is therefore:

$$\sqrt{\tfrac{1}{3}}a(\tfrac{3}{2})\, \Psi(\tfrac{3}{2}, -\tfrac{1}{2}) + \sqrt{\tfrac{2}{3}}a(\tfrac{1}{2})\, \Psi(\tfrac{1}{2}, -\tfrac{1}{2})$$

for both $T$ and $T_3$ are conserved in the reaction. Substituting the expressions for the isotopic spin wave functions, given by (3.21) and (3.19) respectively, we have for the scattered amplitude

$$= \sqrt{\tfrac{1}{3}}a(\tfrac{3}{2})[\sqrt{\tfrac{1}{3}}u_p\pi^- + \sqrt{\tfrac{2}{3}}u_n\pi^0] + \sqrt{\tfrac{2}{3}}a(\tfrac{1}{2})[\sqrt{\tfrac{2}{3}}u_p\pi^- - \sqrt{\tfrac{1}{3}}u_n\pi^0]$$

$$= u_p\pi^- \left[ \frac{a(\tfrac{3}{2}) + 2a(\tfrac{1}{2})}{3} \right] + \sqrt{2}u_n\pi^0 \left[ \frac{a(\tfrac{3}{2}) - a(\tfrac{1}{2})}{3} \right] \qquad (4.4)$$

The first term gives the scattering amplitude for direct scattering (4.2), while the second gives that for charge exchange scattering (4.3). Consider now the cross-sections for the three processes (4.1) to (4.3), which may be either differential or total cross-sections. These cross-sections will be given by the squares of the appropriate scattering amplitudes, so that for, say, the total cross-sections:

$$\sigma_{T^+} \propto |\, a(\tfrac{3}{2})\,|^2 \qquad (4.5)$$

$$\sigma_{T^-} \propto \tfrac{1}{9}|\, 2a(\tfrac{1}{2}) + a(\tfrac{3}{2})\,|^2 \qquad (4.6)$$

$$\sigma_{T^0} \propto \tfrac{2}{9}|\, a(\tfrac{3}{2}) - a(\tfrac{1}{2})\,|^2 \qquad (4.7)$$

It is of interest to consider three particular situations explicitly as follows:

(a) $a(\tfrac{1}{2}) = 0$; $a(\tfrac{3}{2}) \neq 0$   then   $\sigma_{T^+} : \sigma_{T^-} : \sigma_{T^0} :: 9 : 1 : 2$

(b) $a(\tfrac{1}{2}) = a(\tfrac{3}{2}) \neq 0$   then   $\sigma_{T^+} : \sigma_{T^-} : \sigma_{T^0} :: 1 : 1 : 0$

(c) $a(\tfrac{1}{2}) \neq 0$; $a(\tfrac{3}{2}) = 0$   then   $\sigma_{T^+} : \sigma_{T^-} : \sigma_{T^0} :: 0 : 2 : 1$

## Experimental determination of the total cross-sections

The total cross-sections can be measured by a simple attenuation experiment using scintillation counters. Two or more counters may be used to define the pion beam, intensity $I_0$, incident on a liquid hydrogen target; a third counter behind the target detects the unscattered beam of particles, intensity $I$, say. Thus the attenuation, $I/I_0$, of the beam is measured directly; it is related to the total cross-section, $\sigma_T$, by the expressions

$$I = I_0 \exp(-x/\lambda) \quad \text{and} \quad \lambda = 1/N\sigma_T \qquad (4.8)$$

where $\lambda$ is the interaction mean free path, $x$ is the target thickness and $N$ is the number of hydrogen atoms per cm$^3$.

Alternatively a counter telescope may be used to detect the scattered particles at different angles, and the integral of the distribution over all angles is equal to the total cross-section.

Experiments have been carried out using hydrogen-filled diffusion chambers and photographic emulsions to record the individual scattering events. In the latter case the hydrogen normally present in emulsion is used as the target material, and the pion–proton elastic scattering events must be distinguished from collisions with complex nuclei which also give two scattered particles. This may be done by application of the conservation laws. Unfortunately it is difficult to obtain and record a large number of events using these visual techniques; this remark does not apply to hydrogen bubble-chamber experiments, but the problem then is that of the analysis of a large number of individual events. These visual techniques are of particular value for experiments at low energies, where the pions do not have sufficient energy to traverse a counter telescope, either before or after being scattered.

Both counter and visual techniques have been used to investigate positive pion scattering. In the case of negative pions one has to resolve the direct scattering from the charge exchange scattering, so that the neutral pions (or rather, their decay gamma-rays) that are produced, must be detected. This is usually done by placing a suitable radiator in front of a scintillation counter telescope, in order to convert the gamma-rays to electron pairs. A schematic diagram of the apparatus used at Chicago by Anderson, Fermi and others (Anderson *et al.*, 1953) for the original experiments on pion scattering, is shown in Fig. 5. The counters were liquid scintillators;

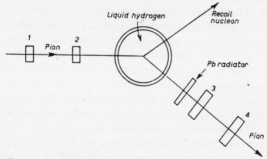

*Fig. 5. Diagrammatic sketch of a scintillation counter experiment to study pion–proton scattering*
(From ANDERSON *et al. Phys. Rev.* **91**, 155 (1953))

those defining the beam were 2″ in diameter while those recording the scattered particles were originally 4″ in diameter and later rectangular, 4″ × 6″. The liquid hydrogen Dewar vessel was about 6″ in diameter. The $\gamma$ rays from $\pi^0$ decay were converted into electron–positron pairs by the $\frac{1}{4}$″ lead converter placed in front of counter 3. The lead was removed for the observation of the direct scattering of both the positive and negative pions. For each angle, and for each energy, measurements were made with and without hydrogen in the Dewar vessel.

The first differential measurements on pion–proton scattering were made by Anderson, Fermi and others at 45°, 90° and 135° laboratory angle for positive pions of 78, 110 and 135 MeV kinetic energy, and at the same angles for 120 and 144 MeV negative pions. The integrated values of the differential cross-sections were in reasonable agreement with the total cross-sections obtained from the earlier transmission experiments.

At 120 MeV, these experiments (Anderson et al., 1952, 1953) yielded the ratio 91 : 11 : 22 for the cross-sections $\sigma_T^+ : \sigma_T^- : \sigma_T^0$. At 144 MeV, the negative pion differential measurements together with later photographic plate work of Orear (1954) on positive pion scattering, gave 158 : 17 : 31 for this ratio. These figures are very close to the 9 : 1 : 2 ratio expected if the scattering is taking place solely through the $T = \frac{3}{2}$ isotopic spin state. This does not mean that $a(\frac{1}{2}) = 0$ but only that $a(\frac{3}{2}) \gg a(\frac{1}{2})$ on the average over all angles, in the energy range 100–150 MeV. These results provided strong evidence for the importance of the $T = \frac{3}{2}$ scattering state.

In the past few years much work has been carried out on the determination of the total cross-sections for positive and negative pions scattered by hydrogen. Some information, particularly below 300 MeV, has come from the integration of data obtained by the visual techniques, but most experiments have been transmission measurements, using liquid hydrogen targets and scintillation counters. The most accurate and extensive work is probably that of Lindenbaum and Yuan (1955) and Cool et al. (1956) at Brookhaven, Ashkin et al. (1956) at Carnegie, and Mukhin et al. (1956) at Dubna; the measurements of Cool et al. extend to 2 GeV, while preliminary data up to 4·4 GeV have been obtained at Berkeley.

The variation of the cross-sections with energy is shown in Fig. 6. We recall that $\sigma_T{}^+$ represents the scattering in a pure $T = \frac{3}{2}$ state

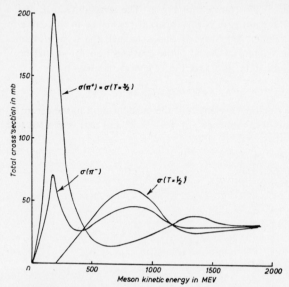

*Fig. 6. The total cross-sections for $\pi^+ + p$ and $\pi^- + p$ scattering, as a function of the kinetic energy of the incident pion*
(Based on data quoted by YUAN. CERN Symposium, II, 195 (1956))

while the negative pion scattering ($\sigma_T{}^- + \sigma_T{}^0$) is a mixture of $T = \frac{1}{2}$ and $T = \frac{3}{2}$ states. In terms of scattering amplitudes we have from (4.4):

Scattering amplitude

$$\text{for } (\pi^- + p \longrightarrow \pi^- + p) = \tfrac{2}{3}a(\tfrac{1}{2}) + \tfrac{1}{3}a(\tfrac{3}{2})$$
$$\text{and for } (\pi^- + p \longrightarrow \pi^0 + n) = -\sqrt{\tfrac{2}{3}}a(\tfrac{1}{2}) + \sqrt{\tfrac{2}{3}}a(\tfrac{3}{2})$$

Adding the absolute squares of these scattering amplitudes yields the total cross-section

$$\sigma_T(\pi^-) = \sigma_T{}^- + \sigma_T{}^0 = \tfrac{2}{3}\,|\,a(\tfrac{1}{2})\,|^{\,2} + \tfrac{1}{3}\,|\,a(\tfrac{3}{2})\,|^{\,2} \qquad (4.9)$$

We can write

$$|\,a(\tfrac{1}{2})\,|^{\,2} = \sigma(T = \tfrac{1}{2}) \quad \text{and} \quad |\,a(\tfrac{3}{2})\,|^{\,2} = \sigma(T = \tfrac{3}{2}) = \sigma_T(\pi^+)$$

Thus

$$\sigma(T = \tfrac{1}{2}) = \tfrac{3}{2}\sigma_T(\pi^-) - \tfrac{1}{2}\sigma_T(\pi^+) \qquad (4.10)$$

and this is also plotted on Fig. 6. The striking feature of the data shown in this figure is the apparent resonance in the curve for $\sigma_{T^+}$ at just under 200 MeV. If this is in fact due to a resonance in a particular state of $J$ and $l$, the cross-section for scattering in this resonance state, as a function of energy, is given by

$$\sigma(J, l) = 2\pi\lambda^2(2J + 1) \qquad (4.11)$$

where $\lambda$ is the wavelength of the incident pion in the centre of mass system.* If $J = \tfrac{3}{2}$ then $\sigma(\tfrac{3}{2}, l) = 8\pi\lambda^2$ and this is plotted in Fig. 7

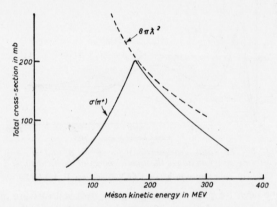

*Fig. 7. The total cross-section for $\pi^+ + p$ scattering, and $8\pi\lambda^2$, as a function of energy*

(From YUAN. *CERN Symposium*, **II**, 195 (1956) )

together with the experimental curve. The two curves meet at the peak, within the experimental errors of the measurements. Thus, we can state that there is a resonance in the state with $T = \tfrac{3}{2}, J = \tfrac{3}{2}$ at a pion bombarding energy of approximately 195 MeV. The implications of this result will be discussed later in this chapter.

---

* In this particular case this expression is most easily obtained by putting $\delta_{33} = 90°$ and $\delta_3 = \delta_{31} = 0°$ in (4.15), page 65.

For the scattering of negative pions, a resonance in the $T = \frac{3}{2}$, $J = \frac{3}{2}$ state would lead to a maximum cross-section of $\sigma_T(\pi^-)_{\text{res}} = 8\pi\lambda^2/3$ for if $a(\frac{1}{2}) = 0$ then $\sigma_T(\pi^-) = \frac{1}{3}\sigma_T(\pi^+)$, from (4.9). The experimental data agrees with this prediction and in fact shows that $a(\frac{1}{2})$ is essentially zero up to 200 MeV. Above this energy $\sigma_T(\pi^-)$ does not drop as sharply as $\sigma_T(\pi^+)$ showing that scattering in the $T = \frac{1}{2}$ state is beginning to play a role. This is shown by the curve for $\sigma(T = \frac{1}{2})$ which is plotted in Fig. 6. The peak in this curve at ~800 MeV suggests another resonance; if this were due to a resonance in a single $J$-state, then from (4.11) the appropriate value of $J$ would be $\frac{7}{2}$ or $\frac{9}{2}$. Alternatively there may be resonances in several $J$-states. Recent photoproduction experiments at gamma-ray energies between 500 and 1000 MeV indicate the existence of a resonance in the $T = \frac{1}{2}$, $J = \frac{3}{2}$, state, at an incident pion energy (for pion–nucleon scattering) of around 600 MeV. It has been suggested by Wilson (1958) that the apparent resonance at 800 MeV (see Fig. 6) may be the combined result at the $T = \frac{1}{2}$, $J = \frac{3}{2}$ resonance at 600 MeV and of a $T = \frac{1}{2}$, $J = \frac{5}{2}$, resonance at around 850 MeV. There appears to be another resonance in the $T = \frac{3}{2}$ state around 1300 MeV; the theoretical implications of this feature of the data are still obscure.

## Differential cross-sections

### (a) Theory

The angular distributions of the pions scattered from hydrogen yield more information than a knowledge of the total cross-sections. For pion–proton scattering the argument given in Chapter III suggests that up to about 200 MeV only partial waves of $l = 0$ and $l = 1$ need be considered. With only one or two angular momentum states involved, the characteristic features of the data are conveniently exhibited by a partial wave analysis. This was first done for pion–proton scattering by Fermi (Anderson *et al.*, 1953).

Consider the scattering of positive pions by protons; in this case only the $T = \frac{3}{2}$ isotopic spin state is involved. For $s$ and $p$ waves only there will be three scattering states of meson and proton, viz. $J = \frac{1}{2}$, $l = 0$, $J = \frac{1}{2}$, $l = 1$ and $J = \frac{3}{2}$, $l = 1$. The scattering amplitudes for these three states can be written as $a_s$, $a_{p1}$ and $a_{p3}$ or generally $a_{l, 2J}$. For an incident wave of given $l$ and $J$, its scattered amplitude at an angle $\theta$ is given by

$$f(\theta) = (2l + 1)\frac{(e^{2i\delta} - 1)}{2i}P_l(\cos \theta)\lambda \quad \text{(from 3.33)}$$

where $\delta$ is the corresponding phase shift.

It is convenient to define a scattering amplitude, $a$, for each value of $l$ and $J$, such that

$$a = (e^{2i\delta} - 1)/2i \quad \text{in units of } \lambda \qquad (4.12)$$

The complete scattering amplitude for the scattering process $\pi^+ + p \longrightarrow \pi^+ + p$ consists of two parts, the direct scattering for which the direction of the nucleon spin is not changed, and the 'spin-flip' scattering for which it is reversed. It may be shown* that the amplitudes for these two processes, $f_1$ and $f_2$ respectively, are given by

$$f_1 = a_s + (2a_{p3} + a_{p1}) \cos \theta$$
and
$$f_2 = (a_{p1} - a_{p3}) \sin \theta \, e^{i\phi}$$

both in units of $\lambda$. Summing the scattering cross-sections, both without and with spin-flip for the target proton, the differential cross-section is

$$\frac{d\sigma}{d\Omega} = \lambda^2 \left\{ |f_1|^2 + |f_2|^2 \right\}$$

Substituting for $f_1$ and $f_2$, and remembering that the scattering amplitudes $a_s$, $a_{p1}$ and $a_{p3}$ are all complex quantities, the expression for $d\sigma/d\Omega$ finally reduces to

$$\frac{d\sigma}{d\Omega} = A + B \cos \theta + C \cos^2 \theta \qquad (4.13)$$

where $A = |a_s|^2 + |a_{p3} - a_{p1}|^2$
$B = 2Rea_s^*(2a_{p3} + a_{p1})$
and $C = 3|a_{p3}|^2 + 6Rea_{p1}^*a_{p3}$

in which $Re$ means real part and an asterisk indicates the complex conjugate.

In terms of phase shifts:

$$\left. \begin{array}{l} A = \sin^2 \delta_3 + \sin^2(\delta_{33} - \delta_{31}) \\ B = 2 \sin \delta_3[2 \sin \delta_{33} \cos(\delta_{33} - \delta_3) + \sin \delta_{31} \cos(\delta_{31} - \delta_3)] \\ C = 3 \sin^2 \delta_{33} + 6 \sin \delta_{31} \sin \delta_{33} \cos(\delta_{33} - \delta_{31}) \end{array} \right\} \qquad (4.14)$$

* Bethe and de Hoffmann, 1955. *Mesons and Fields*. Vol. II, *Mesons*, pp. 63–5.

Here the notation adopted for the phase shifts is that first introduced by Fermi; the phase shifts of the $s$ waves of $T = \frac{1}{2}$ and $T = \frac{3}{2}$ are denoted by $\delta_1$ and $\delta_3$ while the phase shifts of the $p$ waves are denoted by $\delta_{33}$, $\delta_{31}$, $\delta_{13}$ and $\delta_{11}$, where the first index is twice the isotopic spin of the state in question and the second index is twice the total angular momentum $(J)$.

The total cross-section is given by

$$\sigma_{total} = \lambda^2 \int_0^{2\pi} \int_0^{2\pi} (A + B \cos\theta + C \cos^2\theta) \sin\theta \, d\theta \, d\phi$$
$$= 4\pi\lambda^2 (A + C/3)$$
$$= 4\pi\lambda^2 \{\sin^2\delta_3 + \sin^2\delta_{31} + 2\sin^2\delta_{33}\} \quad (4.15)$$

The corresponding expressions for the scattering of negative pions are more complicated since they also involve the $T = \frac{1}{2}$ phase shifts; they are given in Bethe and de Hoffmann, p. 67.

(b) *Experimental results below 400 MeV*

The majority of the experimental work on differential cross-sections for pion–nucleon scattering has been carried out with meson beams

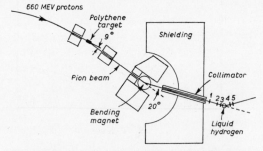

*Fig. 8. Diagrammatic sketch of the experimental arrangement used at the Dubna Laboratory, U.S.S.R., to obtain pion beams for scattering experiments*

(From MUKHIN *et al. CERN Symposium*, **II**, 204 (1956) )

from the large synchro-cyclotrons, using scintillation counter techniques. At very low energies diffusion cloud chambers have been used. The experimental arrangement used by Mukhin *et al.* at Dubna is shown in Fig. 8. The mesons emitted at 9° from a polythene target, bombarded by the external proton beam from the synchrocyclotron, are subsequently bent through 20° by a magnet and pass down a long collimator. This beam is defined by counters 1, 2 and 3 placed before the hydrogen target while the scattered particles are detected by counters 4 and 5.

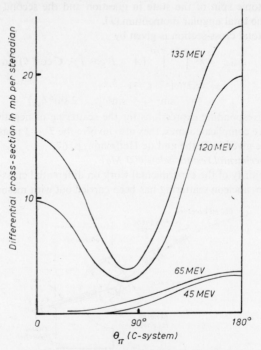

*Fig. 9. Differential cross-sections for $\pi^+ + p$ scattering at a number of energies*

(From data quoted by YUAN. *CERN Symposium,* **II,** 195 (1956))

Typical angular distributions for positive pion scattering between 45 and 135 MeV are shown in Fig. 9. If there was scattering only in the $J = \frac{3}{2}$ state, the dominant state according to the total cross-section data, the coefficient $B$ in (4.13) would be zero and

$$\frac{d\sigma}{d\Omega} = \sin^2 \delta_{33}(1 + 3 \cos^2 \theta)\lambda^2 \qquad (4.16)$$

which is symmetrical about 90°. The data shown in Fig. 9 are clearly
not symmetrical about 90°, which is clear evidence for the existence
of some *s*-wave scattering. In fact it turns out that only a relatively
small amount of *s*-state scattering is required to give the observed
asymmetry. At higher energies the shape of the distribution changes,
becoming more peaked in the forward direction; a typical curve for
307 MeV is shown in Fig. 10.

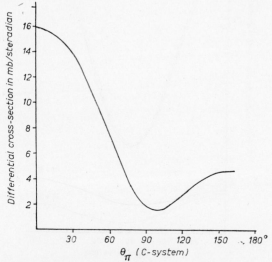

*Fig. 10. Differential cross-section for $\pi^+ + p$ scattering
at 307 MeV*

(From MUKHIN *et al. CERN Symposium,* **II**, 204 (1956) )

The angular distributions for direct and charge exchange scattering of negative pions have been determined at a number of energies.
There is not much reliable data for the charge exchange process,
for the experiments are naturally rather difficult. Fig. 11 shows the
results obtained by Ashkin *et al.* at 170 MeV. The dotted curve in
this figure is three times the sum of the differential cross-sections
for the negative pion scattering processes (4.2) and (4.3). The close
agreement between this curve and that for the scattering of positive

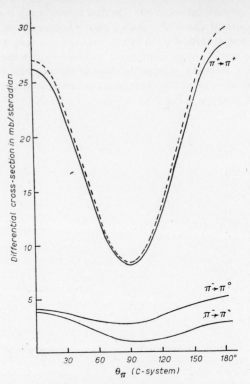

*Fig.* 11. *Differential cross-sections for $\pi^+ + p$ and $\pi^- + p$ scattering at 170 MeV; the dotted curve represents three times the differential cross-section for elastic scattering and charge exchange of negative pions*

(From ASHKIN *et al.* CERN *Symposium,* **II,** 225 (1956) )

pions is a further indication of the dominance of the $T = \frac{3}{2}$ state in the negative pion scattering processes, for equation (4.9) is also valid for differential cross-sections, that is,

$$\frac{d\sigma}{d\Omega}(\pi^- + p \rightarrow \pi^- + p) + \frac{d\sigma}{d\Omega}(\pi^- + p \rightarrow \pi^0 + n)$$

$$= \frac{2}{3} \, |f(T = \tfrac{1}{2}, \theta) \, |^2 + \frac{1}{3} \, |f(T = \tfrac{3}{2}, \theta) \, |^2$$

$$= \frac{1}{3} \frac{d\sigma}{d\Omega}(\pi^+ + p \longrightarrow \pi^+ + p)$$

if $f(T = \tfrac{1}{2}, \theta)$ is zero. This would imply that the three $T = \tfrac{1}{2}$ phase shifts ($\delta_1$, $\delta_{11}$ and $\delta_{13}$) were zero; in fact $\delta_1$ is finite but small and the other two phase shifts are negligibly small at least up to 100 MeV. Above this energy $\delta_{13}$ increases in magnitude with increasing energy.

## Partial wave analysis

A partial wave analysis, at one pion energy, is possible when measurements have been made of the three differential cross-sections at a number of angles. If it is assumed that only $s$- and $p$-waves participate in the scattering, then there are six phase shifts to be determined (see 4.14). Measurements of the cross-sections for the three processes (4.1) to (4.3) at three angles would yield nine equations for the six unknowns, so that in principle the problem is overdetermined. In practice the experimental errors are large and the extra equations are needed in order to reduce the number of possible solutions. The first partial wave analysis of pion–proton scattering was carried out by Fermi (Anderson *et al.*, 1953; Fermi *et al.*, 1954) using the Chicago data at 120 and 135 MeV. The results are shown in the first part of Table 6, together with the $T = \tfrac{3}{2}$ phase shifts at 78 MeV obtained from positive pion scattering data.

A more extensive analysis of the Chicago data was undertaken by de Hoffmann *et al.* (1954), using the Los Alamos Maniac Computer. The angular distributions of negative pions were taken as the primary data, for at that time the positive pion data between 150 and 220 MeV had large errors. The total cross-section for positive pion scattering and some approximate features of the positive pion angular distributions were used as a check. Many sets of the six phase shifts were found to satisfy the experimental data at a given energy, but by using arguments of continuity, together with physical reasoning and some qualitative features of the theory, they decided in favour of the set of phase shifts shown in the second part of Table 6. The third part of this table shows phase shifts deduced

TABLE 6

| Energy MeV | $\delta_3$ | $\delta_1$ | $\delta_{33}$ | $\delta_{31}$ | $\delta_{13}$ | $\delta_{11}$ | Reference |
|---|---|---|---|---|---|---|---|
| 78 | −6 | | +13 | | −3 | | Anderson et al. |
| 120 | −15 | +9 | +30 | +4 | +2 | −3 | (1953) |
| 135 | −14 | +10 | +38 | +2 | +5 | −5 | |
| 120 | −12 | +8 | +30 | +6 | +2 | −4 | de Hoffman |
| 144 | −13 | +14 | +46 | +5 | +3 | −5 | et al. (1954) |
| 169 | −4 | +7 | +64 | +3 | −1 | +7 | |
| 170 | −8 | +10 | +65 | −8 | +2 | 0 | Ashkin et al. |
| 220 | −18 | −8½ | +112 | 0 | +11½ | +3 | (1956), set (ii) |
| 176 | −11 | | +67 | −16 | | | Mukhin et al. |
| 240 | −14 | | +113 | −8 | | | (1956) |
| 307 | −24 | | +134 | −8 | | | |

All values based on assumption of s- and p-waves only.

from more recent data obtained at the Carnegie Institute of Technology and at Dubna. All these sets of phase shifts are characterized by the dominance of $\delta_{33}$, that is, the phase shift for the $J = T = \frac{3}{2}$ state. A solution of this type is known as a Fermi-type solution. The value of $\delta_{33}$ passes through 90° at about 190 MeV which may therefore be taken to be the resonance energy. The corresponding energy in the centre of mass, (C), system of pion and nucleon is about 160 MeV.

## The s-wave phase shifts

These are of particular interest, for at low energies, where only s-waves are important, the interactions involving close approach of the meson and nucleon will not predominate and reliable theoretical calculations may first become possible for simple situations of this kind. Information about $\delta_1$ and $\delta_3$ may be obtained from several different types of experiment, other than the scattering experiments used as a basis for a phase-shift analysis.

Consider the process $\pi^- + p \longrightarrow \pi^- + p$. The scattering amplitude for this process from (4.4) is $\frac{1}{3}\{2a(\frac{1}{2}) + a(\frac{3}{2})\}$. In terms of phase shifts, and for $\delta$ small (low energy), $a = \delta \lambdabar = \delta/\eta$ from (4.12), for each value of $l$ and $J$, where $\eta$ is the momentum of the pion, in units of $m_\pi c$, in the $C$-system. Therefore, considering only $s$-waves, which will be true at zero energy, the differential cross-section for the direct scattering of negative pions is given by the square of the scattering amplitude, viz.

$$\frac{d\sigma}{d\Omega}(\pi^- + p \longrightarrow \pi^- + p) = \frac{1}{9}[2a_1 + a_3]^2 \qquad (4.17)$$

where the notation for the scattering amplitudes is the same as that used for the phase shifts in (4.15). The $s$-wave scattering length, $a_-$, may be defined as

$$a_- = \frac{1}{3}[2a_1 + a_3] = \frac{\lambdabar}{3}[2\delta_1 + \delta_3] \qquad (4.18)$$

Experimentally the differential cross-section must be measured at a finite energy and the expression relating $d\sigma/d\Omega$ to $a_-$ is then rather complicated and involves $\delta_{33}$. It is usual to assume $\delta_{13} = \delta_{31} = \delta_{11} = 0$ as is indicated by the phase-shift analysis discussed earlier. A number of experiments have been carried out at energies between 10 and 30 MeV, which thus give values of $2\delta_1 + \delta_3$ (see Orear (1956) for references).

In principle the difference between $\delta_1$ and $\delta_3$ can be obtained from a measurement of the charge-exchange scattering cross-section for negative pions on hydrogen. At zero energy, the total cross-section is (cf. 4.7)

$$\sigma_T^0(E \sim 0) = 4\pi\lambdabar^2 \frac{v_0}{v_-} \frac{2}{9}(\delta_1 - \delta_3)^2 \qquad (4.19)$$

The factor $v_0/v_-$ is the ratio of velocities, in the $C$-system, of the emitted neutral pion and the incident negative pion, and appears because charge exchange is a nuclear reaction and not pure scattering owing to the $\pi^- - \pi^0$ mass difference. At high energies $v_0/v_- \sim 1$, but at very low energies it is significantly different from unity. $\sigma_T^0(E \sim 0)$ has not been measured but the Panofsky ratio $P = \sigma(\pi^- + p \longrightarrow \pi^0 + n)/\sigma(\pi^- + p \longrightarrow n + \gamma)$ is known. Unfortunately neither the cross-section for $\pi^- + p \longrightarrow n + \gamma$, nor its inverse, have yet been measured directly, but a value can be inferred from a knowledge of the $\pi^+/\pi^-$ photoproduction ratio from deuterium at threshold. Apart from minor corrections (but see below) it may be assumed that

$$T = \frac{\sigma(\gamma + D \longrightarrow \pi^+ + 2n)}{\sigma(\gamma + D \longrightarrow \pi^- + 2p)} \simeq \frac{\sigma(\gamma + p \longrightarrow \pi^+ + n)}{\sigma(\gamma + n \longrightarrow \pi^- + p)} \quad (4.20)$$

T and $\sigma(\gamma + p \longrightarrow \pi^+ + n)$ are known, and therefore $\sigma(\gamma + n \longrightarrow \pi^- + p)$ is determined. Detailed balance gives

$$\sigma(\pi^- + p \longrightarrow n + \gamma) = \frac{p_\gamma^2 \cdot g_\gamma}{p_\pi^2 \; g_\pi} \sigma(n + \gamma \longrightarrow p + \pi^-)$$

where $g_\gamma = 2$, $g_\pi = 1$ are the statistical weights and $p_\gamma$, $p_\pi$ are the relevant momenta. Thus a value for $\delta_1 - \delta_3$, achieved by a rather indirect method, may be evaluated. At a finite energy $\sigma_T{}^0$ can be measured directly, but the experiment is difficult, and has only been carried out by two groups at energies between 20 and 40 MeV. Combining the results of the different experiments which give reliable values for $\delta_3$, $2\delta_1 + \delta_3$ and $\delta_1 - \delta_3$, Orear (1956) found

$$\delta_1 = (0{\cdot}167 \pm 0{\cdot}012)\eta \quad \text{and} \quad \delta_3 = (-0{\cdot}105 \pm 0{\cdot}010)\eta$$

It is of interest to remark that the above argument can be used to determine P from the measured values of T, $\delta_1$ and $\delta_3$. Some care is necessary in obtaining a value for T at zero energy, for the value derived depends upon the exact manner in which the extrapolation of the results, which are determined at a finite energy, is carried out. Dispersion theory suggests that $T = 0{\cdot}75$, which together with $(\delta_1 - \delta_3)$ would give $P = 2{\cdot}43$. This is higher than the directly determined values of P, which lie between $1{\cdot}50$ and $1{\cdot}87$, with quoted errors of between $0{\cdot}10$ and $0{\cdot}15$ (see Chapter II, p. 23). The values of T obtained from the photoproduction experiments are of the order of $0{\cdot}5$, but the extrapolation procedure employed has been questioned by several authors. Further, it has been pointed out by Moravcsik (1958) that to obtain the charge exchange scattering cross-section at zero energy from (4.19) may not be a valid procedure, for at the low energies one might expect violations of charge independence on account of mass differences and Coulomb effects. It is clearly important to investigate these discrepancies.

Values for $\delta_1$ and $\delta_3$ can also be obtained from a study of the level shifts in pi-mesonic atoms. A mesonic atom is one which contains a meson bound in an orbit round the nucleus.* In general pions rapidly fall to the $1s$ orbit and are then captured by the nucleus. The interesting point is that the binding (Coulomb) energy of the $1s$ orbit is modified by the pion nucleus interaction. Thus, there is a certain shift of the level from its position calculated for Coulomb forces only. This shift can be obtained from a measurement of the $2p - 1s$ energy separation, that is, by observation of the X-rays emitted when a meson cascades from the $2p$ to the $1s$ level. An important qualitative result is that the quantity $(\delta_1 + 2\delta_3)/3$ is negative (repulsive). This follows directly from the fact that all the $1s$ levels are shifted upward, that is, the binding energy of the meson is decreased compared with the Rydberg formula. Qualitatively the values obtained for $\delta_1$ and $\delta_3$ agree well with those quoted on the previous page; although they were not used by Orear because they are based on the assumption that the effects of the nucleons in the nucleus on the meson are purely additive.

## Ambiguities in the data

### (a) Fermi–Yang solutions

The ordinary scattering data cannot distinguish between the phase shifts shown in Table 6 and a set characterized by a reversal of the sign of $(\delta_{31} - \delta_{33})$, which will give a resonance in the (31) state. This latter set of phase shifts is known as the Yang solution. A measurement of the polarization of the recoil proton would, in principle, decide between the two sets, since the two types of solution predict quite different polarizations. Experiments to do this have recently been carried out. The results of Ashkin *et al.* (1959) at a pion energy of 223 MeV, agree best with the Fermi set of phase shifts which has $\delta_1$ positive. A positive value for $\delta_1$ is consistent with the linear relationship between $\delta_1$ and $\eta$, proposed by Orear. The statistical accuracy of the experiment does not permit the exclusion

---

* e.g. see Stearns and Stearns (1956); Stearns (1957).

of the Yang set of phase shifts with $\delta_1$ negative. There is, however, a strong theoretical argument, based on the dispersion relations (see p. 82) against phase shifts of the Yang type.

(b) *The absolute sign of the phase shifts*

Only the relative signs of the phase shifts can be determined from an analysis of the ordinary scattering data. To obtain the absolute signs it is necessary to measure the interference of the nuclear scattering

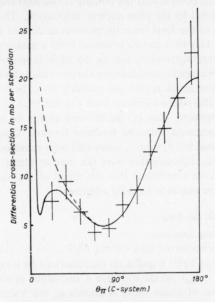

*Fig. 12. Differential cross-section for $\pi^+ + p$ scattering at 124 MeV; the full curve is for destructive interference between the Coulomb and nuclear scattering, while the dotted curve is for constructive interference*

(From FERRETTI *et al. Nuovo Cimento*, **1**, 1238 (1955))

with another scattering of known sign, such as Coulomb scattering. This is repulsive for positive pions and destructive interference would indicate attractive nuclear scattering.

Coulomb effects are most important at small angles, and therefore a visual technique offers the easiest experimental approach to utilize. The existence of destructive interference was first convincingly demonstrated by Puppi and collaborators (Ferretti *et al.*, 1955; Ferrari *et al.*, 1956) from a study of the scattering of positive pions with energies between 70 and 130 MeV by the free hydrogen present in nuclear emulsions. The experimental results for the differential cross-section at 124 MeV, based on 502 events, is shown in Fig. 12. The data was first analysed by computing the phase shifts, using only those events with $\theta > 45°$ ($\theta$ is the angle of scatter of the meson in the *C*-system), where Coulomb effects can be neglected. The complete solutions, with the Coulomb terms, corresponding to the two alternatives in sign, were then computed, using the formulae given by Solmitz (1954); these are shown by the dotted line (constructive interference) and by the full line (destructive interference). The experimental depression of the cross-section in the forward direction clearly favours a choice of sign such that $\delta_{33}$ is positive and $\delta_3$ is negative. Quantitatively, in the angular interval 15–30°, which was not used in calculating the phase shifts, the two solutions would predict 26 and 38 events respectively; the number observed was 24. The statistical weight of these data is not high, but more extensive measurements between 70 and 130 MeV agree well with the assumption of destructive interference.

## The variation with energy of the phase shifts

The dominant *p*-wave phase shift is that for the $T = \frac{3}{2}$, $J = \frac{3}{2}$ state, that is, $\delta_{33}$; $\delta_{31}$ appears to be small at least up to 200 MeV, while $\delta_{13}$ is small to 100 MeV but becomes positive and increases in magnitude above this energy. It can be shown that at low energies the phase shifts for a given *l*-value might be expected to vary with $\eta$ as $\eta^{2l+1}$ (Fermi, 1955). Therefore $\delta_{33}$ should vary as $\eta^3$ and below 80 MeV in fact it varies with momentum as $0.235\eta^3$ but at higher energies $\delta_{33}$ increases faster than is predicted by this simple formula, and passes through 90° at between 190 and 195 MeV (see Fig. 13). The resonance in this $T = J = \frac{3}{2}$ state has naturally led to the concentration of meson theory upon this particular state.

Similarly we might expect a linear relationship between $\delta_1$ and $\delta_3$

and momentum. The linear relationships proposed by Orear (1956) have already been mentioned (p. 72); that for $\delta_3$ appears to hold at least 310 MeV, provided that the phase shift analysis is extended to include the $d$ waves (Mukhin *et al.*, 1956) (see Fig. 13). The condition that the phase shifts are proportional to $\eta$ is that the radius, $r_0$, of the meson–nucleon interaction is shorter than the meson wavelength in the $C$-system. Consequently a linear dependence of $\delta_3$ on $\eta$ up to 300 MeV suggests that $r_0$ cannot be much larger than

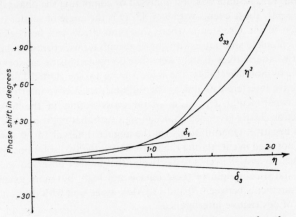

*Fig. 13. The phase shifts $\delta_1$, $\delta_3$ and $\delta_{33}$ as a function of $\eta$, the momenum of the incident pion, in the C-system, in units of $m_\pi c$. The behaviour of $\delta_1$ is uncertain above $\eta \sim 1.5$*

$\lambda$ (300 MeV) $= 6.5 \times 10^{-14}$ cm. The linear relation between $\delta_1$ and $\eta$ appears to hold to about 150 MeV, but above this energy its behaviour is not well determined. The experiment of Ashkin *et al.*, mentioned on page 73, taken in conjunction with the dispersion relations, shows that $\delta_1$ is positive at 223 MeV.

The most interesting feature of the data is that $\delta_1$ and $\delta_3$ have opposite sign (at least up to 150 MeV), in other words, the $s$-wave phase-shifts have a strong isotopic spin dependence. At present this is difficult to explain on theoretical grounds. The behaviour with energy of $\delta_1$ and $\delta_3$ above 150 MeV is also of considerable interest; the explanation of this behaviour has yet to be given.

## Pion scattering at energies above 400 MeV

The highest energy at which counter determinations have been made of differential cross-sections for pion–nucleon scattering is 340 MeV, carried out at Dubna. Above this energy, the pion beams are obtained using protons from the large proton synchrotrons; the intensity of these beams is low and therefore a visual technique must be used for differential measurements. Hydrogen-filled diffusion chambers, hydrogen and propane bubble chambers, and emulsions, have all been used by different investigators, at pion energies up to 5·0 GeV. As the energy rises the proportion of inelastic events (pion production) also rises. For example, at 700 MeV 60% of the positive pion interactions are elastic scatterings (Good *et al.*, 1956) and this fraction has fallen to 20% at 5·0 GeV (Maenchen *et al.*, 1956). The angular distribution in the $C$-system for the elastic events is strongly peaked forward, but there is also a hump at the backward angles. The forward peak can be interpreted as diffraction scattering by a 'black disc' nucleon. Much more data is needed before any definite conclusions can be reached. Similarly the information on pion–nucleon inelastic scattering is meagre and will not be discussed here.

## Theoretical analysis of the experimental data

### (a) Phenomenological analysis

The fundamental field theory of the pion–nucleon interaction cannot be said to be on a firm basis at the present time. For this reason there has grown up during the past few years a phenomenological theory of pion interactions, largely due to the work of Brueckner, Gell-Mann and Watson.

We have seen that the characteristic feature of the experimental data is the existence of a resonant state of $J = \frac{3}{2}$, $T = \frac{3}{2}$, between pion and nucleon. Very soon after Yukawa's postulate of the pion, certain forms of meson theory, which assumed a strong coupling between pions and nucleons, were shown to predict the existence of nuclear isobars, that is, excited states of the nucleon. These excited states would decay to a nucleon and a pion and they would either be stable or unstable, depending on the strength of the coupling. Now, the earlier data on the photoproduction of pions obtained in 1950 and 1951, showed that the cross-sections for the production of charged and neutral pions by photons were approximately the same. This result was not explicable by the theories which assumed a weak coupling between pions and nucleons. It was therefore suggested by Brueckner and Case (1951) that the strong coupling theory should be applied to the problem. In particular they investigated the effects of the existence of nucleon isobars, which is one of the most characteristic features of strong coupling theory, and found that a simple model incorporating isobars gave correctly the general features and magnitude of the cross-section for neutral pion production. Further, the isobars were predicted to be unstable with an excitation energy of several hundred MeV. Subsequently the early experiments on pion–nucleon scattering were carried out, and Brueckner (1952) was able to show that the data could be readily explained in terms of a resonant pion–nucleon interaction corresponding to a nucleon isobar with $J = \frac{3}{2}$, $T = \frac{3}{2}$, and an excitation energy of 277 MeV. This interpretation of the data has been fully confirmed by the later experiments, which we have discussed in this chapter. The essential point, however, is that a resonant pion–nucleon interaction of some kind is a natural consequence of strong coupling theory.

Gell-Mann and Watson (1954) developed a phenom–ological model of pion interactions, based on three fundamental assumptions:

(1) The pion–nucleon interactions have a finite range.

(2) Charge independence is valid, that is, isotopic spin is conserved.

(3) The $J = \frac{3}{2}$, $T = \frac{3}{2}$ state of the pion–nucleon system is one of especially strong and attractive interaction.

The first assumption has specific consequences. When only one orbital angular momentum state is important for an emitted or absorbed particle, then it can be shown that the energy dependence of the cross-section is uniquely determined at low energies. For example, denoting the momentum of the pion in the $C$-system by $q$, the cross-section of a reaction leading to the production of a pion with one accompanying particle in the final state (e.g. $p + p \rightarrow d + \pi^+$), will vary as $q^{2l+1}$, whereas for the elastic scattering of a pion, the cross-section will vary as $q^{4l}$ (see Fermi, 1955).

The fact that only one or two angular momentum states are important at low energies also means that conservation of angular momentum and of parity will be especially important. If the emission and absorption of single mesons by nucleons is the dominant virtual process, then these two conservation laws require that the pions must be emitted predominantly in $p$ states (see Chapter III, p. 51). Gell-Mann and Watson showed that all the major characteristics of the experimental data, both on pion–nucleon scattering, and on the photoproduction of pions from nucleons, could be accounted for on the basis of the assumptions discussed above. For example, the energy dependence of the cross-sections for pion scattering were consistent with the assumption that the pions were predominantly scattered in states of $l = 1$. However, this approach to the problem is phenomenological in origin, and to obtain further information it is necessary to consider in more detail the predictions of meson field theory.

(b) *Field theory*

It has already been mentioned in Chapter III (p. 52) that two theories in particular have received considerable attention. The first of these is the relativistic, symmetric pseudo-scalar meson theory, sometimes called the $\gamma_5$ theory. Although this is a possibly correct physical theory, the large value of the pseudo-scalar coupling constant, $G$, makes calculations almost impossible. This is in contrast to the situation which exists in quantum electrodynamics where the coupling constant $e^2/\hbar c \sim 1/137$; expansions in powers of this coupling constant rapidly converge.

The second theory is that developed originally by Chew, which depends on two parameters, the pseudo-vector coupling constant $f^2$ and a cut-off energy $\omega_m$. The cut-off energy is related to the source radius, $\rho$, discussed on page 52, by the expression $\rho = \hbar c/\omega_m$. It has proved possible to reproduce the major features of the data and to locate the resonance energy at approximately the right point, by choosing suitable values of the coupling constant and of the cut-off energy.

Now, if phase-shift analysis is used to describe the scattering, the scattering amplitude for a given partial wave depends on the quantity $(e^{i\delta_\alpha} \sin \delta_\alpha/p)$ where $\alpha$ denotes the $(T, J)$ state being considered and $p$ is the momentum of the meson. A convenient real quantity to consider is the real part of the inverse of this expression, which is $p \cot \delta_a$. A calculation using perturbation theory with the interaction (3.49) is found to give

$$p \cot \delta_a = \frac{3}{p^2 n_a} \cdot \frac{1}{f^2} \omega \qquad (4.21)$$

where $\omega$ is the total energy of the meson, $f^2$ is the pseudo-vector coupling constant, and $n_a = -8$ for the $(1, 1)$ state, $-2$ for the $(1, 3)$ and $(3, 1)$ states, and $+4$ for the $(3, 3)$ state.

In electrodynamics it is well known that the scattering amplitude for Compton scattering is given correctly by perturbation theory in the limit $\omega \simeq 0$, i.e. for very soft photons. In fact, observation of the low-energy Compton scattering cross-section provides a direct method for determination of the electrodynamical coupling constant, $e^2/\hbar c$. In meson theory, however, the point $\omega = 0$ is not experimentally accessible, as the total energy of the meson is always greater than its rest mass energy $m_\pi c^2$. For physically accessible $\omega$, it is reasonable to assume that (4.21) provides the first term in an expansion in powers of $\omega$; thus for the $(3, 3)$ state

$$\frac{p^3 \cot \delta_{33}}{\omega} \cdot \frac{n_a}{3} \cdot f^2 = 1 - \frac{\omega}{\omega_a} \cdots \qquad (4.22)$$

Retaining only the linear term (consistent with the experimental data up to 250 MeV, as we shall see), the constant $\omega_\alpha$ is then the value of $\omega$ at which $\cot \delta_{33} = 0$, i.e. at which $\delta_{33}$ passes through resonance. The expression therefore provides a very convenient representation for the phase shift $\delta_{33}$. There are good theoretical reasons for an equation of this form; for example, further straightforward calculation of $e^{i\delta} \sin \delta / p$ is consistent with it. Equation (4.22) was first suggested by Low (1955) and derived (Chew and Low, 1956) by making the assumptions only of (i) charge symmetry, (ii) $p$-wave mesons, (iii) a fixed source, (iv) causality* and (v) relativistic invariance, without any further serious theoretical approximations. These authors showed that the accuracy of the formula is improved, and allows to some extent for the nucleon recoil, if $\omega$ is

* See page 82.

replaced by $\omega^* = \omega + p^2/2M$, where $M$ is the nucleon mass. The equations of Chew and Low are closely related to the dispersion relations of classical optics. The fact that such an expression depends more on such fundamental ideas, and less on explicit methods of calculation, makes it a more convincing form, since the great strength of the pion–nucleon coupling compared with that for electrodynamics makes simple theoretical approaches rather suspect. The plot of $p^3 \cot \delta/\omega$ as a function of $\omega$ should therefore be a straight line, and is found to be so experimentally to a high degree of accuracy up to around 250 MeV. Fig. 14 shows a plot of

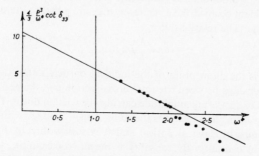

*Fig. 14. A Chew-Low plot of $\frac{4}{3}p^3 \cot \delta_{33}/\omega^*$ against $\omega^*$*
(From PUPPI and STANGHELLINI. *Nuovo Cimento*, **5**, 1305 (1957))

$\frac{4}{3}p^3 \cot \delta_{33}/\omega^*$ against $\omega^*$ for the experimental points available early in 1957. The extrapolation to $\omega^* = 0$ gives $f^2 = 0.095 \pm 0.006$ and the resonance energy $\omega_a^* = 2.22 \pm 0.20$ in units of the pion rest mass. The points begin to deviate from the line above 300 MeV, presumably because the assumption of no recoil begins to be very unrealistic.

The expression (4.22) leads to a resonance curve for the cross-section following the Breit–Wigner formula, well known in the theory of nuclear reactions, provided only that the variation of $\omega$ on the left-hand side of (4.22) should be neglected in the neighbourhood of the resonance. This is easily shown by replacing the $\omega$ by $\omega_a$ and solving for $|\sin^2 \delta|$. Such a formula gives a good fit to the

G

experimental data from 0 to 300 MeV (e.g. see Gell-Mann and Watson, 1954).

## Application of the dispersion relations

Earlier in this chapter it has been shown that the scattering amplitude at any angle can be obtained from the measured cross-sections via the phase shifts. A relationship between the imaginary part of the forward scattering amplitude $Im f(0)$ and the total cross-section, $\sigma_t$, is obtained from the application of the conservation of probability to the description of the scattering process. In this context the conservation of probability is simply the statement that when particles in an incident beam strike a scatterer, they are either scattered or go straight on. The relationship is

$$\sigma_t = \frac{4\pi}{k} Im f(0) \tag{3.35b}$$

where $k$ is the momentum of the incident particle in the $C$-system.

Relationships between the total cross-section and the real part of the forward scattering amplitude can also be written down. They are known as dispersion relations (because of their analogy with similar relationships in classical optics) and they follow directly from the concept of causality. By causality is meant, for example, that the scattered wave should have zero amplitude until the incident wave reaches the scatterer. In the field of electrodynamics, the concept of causality implies that given the state of a system at some zero of time, then what happens at any subsequent time can be calculated. The derivation of the pion–nucleon dispersion relations is beyond the scope of this book, but we may quote one of them to show the form that they take. For example, the dispersion relation for positive pions of momentum, $k$, and total energy, $\omega$, in the laboratory system, has the form

$$D_+(k) - \left(1 + \frac{\omega}{m_\pi c^2}\right) D_+(0) - \frac{1}{2}\left(1 - \frac{\omega}{m_\pi c^2}\right) D_-(0)$$
$$= \frac{k^2}{4\pi^2} P \int_{m_\pi c^2}^{\omega} \frac{d\omega'}{k'} \left[\frac{\sigma_+(\omega')}{\omega' - \omega} + \frac{\sigma_-(\omega')}{\omega' + \omega}\right] + \frac{2f^2}{m_\pi^2 c^4} \cdot \frac{k^2}{\omega^2 - \frac{m_\pi^2 c^4}{2M}} \tag{4.23}$$

In this equation $D_+(k)$ is the real part of the forward scattering amplitude for positive pions of momentum $k$, $D_+(0)$ and $D_-(0)$ that for positive and negative pions respectively of zero momentum, $\sigma_+(\omega')$ and $\sigma_-(\omega')$ are the total cross-sections as a function of energy, for positive and negative mesons, and $f^2$ is the coupling constant (see Goldberger et al., 1955). P denotes that the principal part of the integral is to be taken (see Jeffries and Jeffries (1946), p. 348). The right-hand side of (4.23) can be evaluated numerically if required if the total cross-sections are known. These dispersion relations can be used to give a basis for the analysis of Chew and Low discussed in the preceding section.

The direct use of the dispersion relations may be illustrated by considering positive pion scattering (see, for example, Anderson et al., 1955). If it is assumed that the contributions of $\sigma_+(\omega')$ and $\sigma_-(\omega')$ to the integral in (4.23) are small above 2 GeV (the highest energy at which good measurements were available in 1955), then $D_+(k)$ can be plotted as a function of energy, for an assumed value of the coupling constant. $D_+(0)$ and $D_-(0)$, the real parts of the forward scattering amplitudes at zero energy, are given by a knowledge of the scattering lengths $a_1$ and $a_3$. $D_+(k)$ may also be calculated from a knowledge of the phase shifts at any given energy, $\omega$. The values of $D_+(k)$ so obtained should, of course, fall on the line calculated from the total cross-sections. Anderson et al. found with $f^2 = 0.08$ the fit was much better for the Fermi set of phase shifts than for the Yang set. Further developments of the theory show that not only $D$ but its derivative with respect to angle can be related to the cross-sections, in a manner similar to that given above. It has been shown that application of these new relations gives even more decisive evidence in favour of the Fermi solution (e.g. Davidon and Goldberger, 1956).

The dispersion relations have also been of value in emphasizing contradictions in the experimental data. For example Puppi and Stanghellini (1957) found, by looking at $D_-(k)$ for negative pion scattering, that some of the data fitted the dispersion relation for values of $f^2$ around $0.04$, and not for $f^2 \simeq 0.08$ which is indicated by the experiments on positive pion scattering by protons. Data of much improved accuracy is required before this apparent contradiction can be resolved.

## BIBLIOGRAPHY

BETHE, H. A. and DE HOFFMANN, F. 1955. *Mesons and Fields*, **II.** *Mesons*. Sections 29, 32, 33, 34. Row Peterson.

DALITZ, R. H. 1955. *Progress in Nuclear Physics*, **4**, 95.

DZHELEPOV, V. P. and PONTECORVO, B. M. 1957. *Atomnaya Energiya*, **3**, 413 (English translation in *Journal of Nuclear Energy*, **7**, 129, 1958). Review of work on the Dubna 660 MeV synchro-cyclotron.

FERMI, E. 1955. *Nuovo Cimento*, **II**, Supplemento No. 1 (Varenna lectures, 1954), 17.

GELL-MANN, M. and WATSON, K. M. 1954. *Ann. Rev. Nuc. Sci.* **4**, 219.

JACKSON, J. D. 1958. *The Physics of Elementary Particles*. Princeton University Press.

LOW, F. E. 1957. *Rev. Mod. Phys.* **29**, 216.

STEARNS, M. B. 1957. *Progress in Nuclear Physics*, **6**, 108 (mesonic atoms).

## REFERENCES

ANDERSON, H. L., DAVIDON, W. C. and KRUSE, U. E. 1955. *Phys. Rev.* **100**, 339.

ANDERSON, H. L., FERMI, E., LONG, E. A., MARTIN, R. and NAGLE, D. E. 1952. *Phys. Rev.* **85**, 934.

ANDERSON, H. L., FERMI, E., MARTIN, R. and NAGLE, D. E. 1952. *Phys. Rev.* **85**, 935, 936; 1953. ibid. **91**, 155.

ASHKIN, J., BLASER, J. P., BURGER, A., KUNZE, J. and ROMANOW-SKI, T. A. 1959. To be published.

ASHKIN, J., BLASER, J. P., FEINER, F. and STERN, M. O. 1956. *CERN Symposium*, **II**, p. 225; 1956. *Phys. Rev.* **101**, 1149; 1957. ibid. **105**, 724.

BRUECKNER, K. A. and CASE, K. M. 1951. *Phys. Rev.* **83**, 1141.

BRUECKNER, K. A. 1952. *Phys. Rev.* **86**, 106.

CHEW, G. F. 1954. *Phys. Rev.* **95**, 1669.

HEW, G. F. and LOW, F. E. 1956. *Phys. Rev.* **101**, 1570, 1579.

COOL, R., PICCIONI, O. and CLARK, R. 1956. *Phys. Rev.* **103**, 1082.

DAVIDON, W. C. and GOLDBERGER, M. L. 1956. *Phys. Rev.* **104**, 1119.

FERMI, E., METROPOLIS, N. and ALEI, E. 1954. *Phys. Rev.* **95**, 1581.

FERMI, E. 1955. *Nuovo Cimento*, **II**, Supplemento No. 1, 39.

FERRETTI, L., MANARESI, E., PUPPI, G., QUARENI, G. and RANZI, A. 1955. *Nuovo Cimento*, **I**, 1238.

GELL-MANN, M. and WATSON, K. M. 1954. *Ann. Rev. Nuc. Sci.* **4**, 219.

GOLDBERGER, M. L., MIYAZAWA, H. and OEHME, R. 1955. *Phys. Rev.* **99**, 986.

GOOD, M. L., BRADNER, H., CRAWFORD, F. S. and STEVENSON, M. L. 1956. *Bull. Am. Phys. Soc.* **1**, 174.

JEFFRIES, H. and JEFFRIES, B. S. 1946. *Methods of Mathematical Physics*, 348. C.U.P.

LINDENBAUM, S. J. and YUAN, L. C. L. 1955. *Phys. Rev.* **100**, 306.

LOW, F. E. 1955. *Phys. Rev.* **97**, 1392.

MAENCHEN, G., FOWLER, W. B., POWELL, W. M. and WRIGHT, R. W. 1956. *Bull. Am. Phys. Soc.* **1**, 386.

MORAVCSIK, M. J. 1958. *Phys. Rev.* **111**, 1657.

MUKHIN, A. I., OZEROV, E. B., PONTECORVO, B. M., GRIGORIEV, E. L. and MITIN, N. A. 1956. *CERN Symposium*, **II**, 204.

OREAR, J. 1954. *Phys. Rev.* **96**, 176; 1956. *Nuovo Cimento*, **IV**, 856.

PUPPI, G. and STANGHELLINI. 1957. *Nuovo Cimento*, **V**, 1305.

SOLMITZ, F. T. 1954. *Phys. Rev.* **94**, 1799.

STEARNS, M. and STEARNS, M. B. 1956. *Phys. Rev.* **103**, 1534.

YUAN, L. C. L. 1956. *CERN Symposium*, **II**, 195.

WILSON, R. R. 1958. *CERN Conference Proceedings*, 86-7.

# CHAPTER V

# The Photoproduction of Pions
# from Nucleons

The basic processes of pion production by photons incident on nucleons are

$$\gamma + p \begin{cases} n + \pi^+ & (5.1) \\ p + \pi^0 & (5.2) \end{cases}$$

and

$$\gamma + n \begin{cases} p + \pi^- & (5.3) \\ n + \pi^0 & (5.4) \end{cases}$$

Reactions (5.3) and (5.4) have been studied indirectly, using deuterium as the target material and the interpretation of the data requires some assumptions about the influence of the binding forces in the deuteron. We will consider only reactions (5.1) and (5.2) in this chapter. The gamma-ray threshold energy for pion production is 150 MeV (corresponding to the pion rest mass in the $C$-system). Unfortunately all electron accelerators yield a continuous spectrum of gamma-rays up to $E_\gamma$-max where $E_\gamma$ is the energy of the gamma-ray in the laboratory system. This difficulty can be largely overcome since only two particles are involved in the final state and a measurement of two quantities enables the energy of the incident photon to be calculated.

The cross-sections for pion photoproduction are quite small ($\sim 10^{-28}$ cm$^2$) compared with those for pion nucleon scattering ($10^{-25}$–$10^{-26}$ cm$^2$), but in the latter case the pions have first to be produced in nucleon–nucleon or nucleon–nucleus collisions. Thus, the two types of experiment, photoproduction and pion scattering, are of approximately equal difficulty and yield data of comparable statistical weight. There is a close connexion between them, which will be briefly discussed later.

## Experimental methods

Table 1 shows that most high-energy electron synchrotrons are situated in the U.S.A., and a large amount of work on photo-production has been carried out using these machines, particularly those at Berkeley, California Institute of Technology, Illinois, Massachusetts Institute of Technology and Cornell. The techniques employed have been mostly fast coincidence counter arrays at $E_\gamma > 200$ MeV, and photographic plates below this energy.

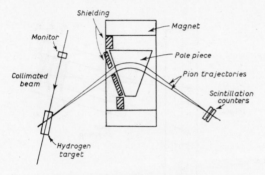

*Fig. 15. Diagrammatic sketch of magnet spectrometer to record pions from $\gamma + p$ collisions*

(From OAKLEY and WALKER. *Phys. Rev.* **97**, 1283 (1955) )

Consider the production of positive pions from hydrogen, reaction (5.1). This is a two-body process and a measurement of the angle and energy of the emitted meson enables the energy of the incident photon to be calculated. Two different counter arrangements have been widely used to detect the charged pion. One is essentially a magnetic spectrometer; for example, the apparatus used by Oakley and Walker (1955) is sketched in Fig. 15. The gamma-ray beam was incident on a target of hydrogen gas under pressure, and a system of slits accepted particles emitted from the target at a given angle. These particles passed between the pole pieces of a magnet giving a maximum field of about 15 kgauss. A second slit system on the far side of the magnetic field defined particles of a small momentum spread which then passed through two scintillation counters in series, connected in coincidence. A pulse height analysis of the signals from the first counter enabled the energy loss of each particle in this counter to be measured. For a given momentum the pulse height distributions for electrons, pions and protons were found to be well separated. As an additional safeguard, a small thickness of lead could be placed between the two counters in order to stop the proton component in the beam reaching the second counter. The angle of emission of the pion is defined by the geometry of the

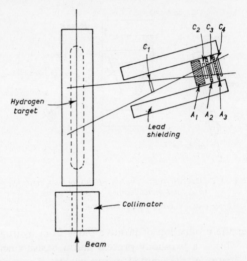

*Fig. 16. Diagrammatic sketch of range telescope to record pions from $\gamma + p$ collisions*
(From TOLLESTRUP *et al. Phys. Rev.* **99**, 220 (1955))

apparatus; it is identified by momentum and energy loss measurements, and the energy spectrum (for a specified value of $E_\gamma$) is determined by measuring the counting rate from the scintillators as a function of the strength of the magnetic field. Integration over the complete energy spectrum gives the differential cross-section at the angle investigated.

An alternative method of determining the energy of a pion is to measure its range in an absorber. The arrangement used by Tolle-strup *et al.* (1955) is shown schematically in Fig. 16. It consisted of four scintillation counters ($C_1$–$C_4$) in series; variable thicknesses of copper $A_1$, $A_2$ and $A_3$, could be placed in front of the second, third and fourth counters. Coincidences $C_1 + C_2 + C_3$, together with an anticoincidence from $C_4$, will correspond to the passage of a particle whose range is between $R =$ thickness $(C_1 + A_1 + C_2 + A_2)$ and $R + dR =$ thickness $(C_1 + A_1 + C_2 + A_2 + C_3 + A_3)$. A pulse height analysis of the signals from the second counter enabled pions to be distinguished from protons. The energy of the pion is given by use of the known range–energy relation for copper.

Photographic emulsions have proved particularly useful for re-cording low-energy mesons for experiments near to the energy threshold for pion production. The energy of the pions is given by their range in the emulsion, while they may be unambiguously identified by observation of the $\pi$–$\mu$ decay process when they come to rest. Experiments of this type are particularly associated with the name of Bernardini (Bernardini and Goldwasser, 1954a, b).

To investigate the production of neutral pions from hydrogen, four approaches are possible, viz. detection of

  (i) the recoiling proton only
 (ii) one gamma-ray only (from the decay of the pion)
(iii) both gamma-rays in coincidence
 (iv) the recoil proton and one gamma ray in coincidence.

Method (i) has been fairly extensively used, although it suffers from the disadvantages that most of the recoil protons are concentrated in the forward direction, while those that are scattered at large angles have rather low energies. Oakley and Walker (1955) have used a magnet spectrometer (Fig. 15) to detect the protons. This method is capable of giving good statistics, but it is necessary to show that protons from processes other than (5.2) do not contribute materially to the counting rate. The experimental procedure adopted is similar to that employed in the case in which the charged pions are detected. Photographic emulsions have also been used to detect the recoil protons. For details, reference may be made to the work of Gold-schmidt-Clermont *et al.* (1955), and of McDonald *et al.* (1957).

Method (ii) is of value only for determining total cross-sections, for the detection of only one gamma-ray does not give sufficient information for differential cross-sections to be obtained. Method (iii) was used to demonstrate the existence of the neutral pion. It suffers from the disadvantage of giving very low counting rates which makes it unsuitable for differential measurements. Method (iv) has been used by some groups (e.g. Walker *et al.*, 1955) but probably does not yield such accurate results as the magnet spectrometer experiments. This is because (*a*) the absolute efficiency of the photon counter enters into the expression for the cross-section, and (*b*) the requirement of a photon coincidence makes the counting rates low. The photons are usually detected by two scintillation counters in anticoincidence, the photon being converted in a thin lead sheet between the counters, while the energy of the associated proton can be measured using a counter telescope of the form shown in Fig. 16.

## Total cross-sections

The total cross-sections for the production of positive and neutral pions from protons are shown in Fig. 17. In general the data has been derived from the measured differential cross-sections. In the case of neutral pion production it has been assumed that the angular distribution can be expressed as $A + B \cos \theta + C \cos^2 \theta$ whereas for charged pion production equation (5.6) has been used. The most striking feature of the data shown in Fig. 17 is the resonance in the cross-section for neutral pion production, which occurs at almost the same centre of mass energy as for the pion–nucleon resonant state. The most direct interpretation of the photoproduction resonance is that it arises from the $T = \frac{3}{2}, J = \frac{3}{2}$ state of the pion–nucleon system. In fact the first direct evidence for a strong attractive interaction between pion and nucleon in this state came from the early photoproduction experiments (see p. 77). The neutral pion data exhibits directly the structure of the pion–nucleon interaction, for the neutral pion has no charge and cannot interact directly with the electromagnetic field. The energy dependence of the cross-section near threshold is proportional to $\eta^3$, that is, a *p*-wave dependence for the emitted pion.

The variation with energy of the cross-section for positive pion production also shows a resonance, but one which is complicated by the interaction between the charge of the pion and the electromagnetic field. It occurs at a slightly lower energy than the neutral

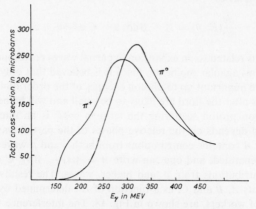

*Fig. 17. The total cross-sections for $\pi^0$ production ($\sigma_T{}^0$) and $\pi^+$ production ($\sigma_T{}^+$) as a function of the energy of the incident gamma ray, $E\gamma$, measured in the laboratory system*

(Based on data from MCDONALD *et al. Phys. Rev.* **107**, 577 (1957); KOESTER and MILLS. *Phys. Rev.* **105**, 1900 (1957); and TOLLESTRUP *et al. Phys. Rev.* **99**, 220 (1955) )

pion resonance. Near threshold the energy dependence of the cross-section is proportional to $\eta$, that is, the pions are predominantly emitted into $s$-states. The mechanism of this process will be discussed later.

## The differential cross-sections

As in the case of pion–nucleon scattering, the differential measurements yield more detailed information than the total cross-sections. Consider first the process $\gamma + p \longrightarrow p + \pi^0$. The angular distributions of the neutral pions from this reaction are not easy to measure for reasons which have already been mentioned. Nevertheless, a considerable amount of work has been carried out from the threshold energy to about 500 MeV. Work at energies higher than this has begun only recently, with the advent of the more energetic electron accelerators (see Table 1). For neutral pion production the differential cross-section, at a given value of $E_\gamma$, can be written in terms of a series

$$\frac{d\sigma}{d\Omega}(E_\gamma, \theta) = A + B\cos\theta + C\cos^2\theta + \ldots \quad (5.5)$$

and this is related to an expansion in partial waves corresponding to the various angular momenta. Since it is believed that only $s$ and $p$ waves are important up to photon energies of the order of 400 MeV the terms after the third are likely to be small and will be neglected. As in pion–proton scattering the term in $\cos\theta$ is an interference term and depends on the relative phases of the partial waves. The quantity $A$ contains contributions from both $s$ and $p$ waves, which can be separated, and one can write $A = A(s) + A(p)$; $C$ contains only contributions from $p$, and higher, waves. The results for the coefficients $A$, $B$ and $C$, as a function of $E_\gamma$, determined by several groups of workers, are shown in Fig. 18. The interference term, $B$, is very small and confirms the smallness of the $s$-wave contribution to the cross-section. $C$ is large, confirming the prediction from the total cross-section results that $p$-wave meson emission is the dominant process; this is also reflected in the large value of $A$, which is almost entirely due to $A(p)$.

The angular distribution of the charged pions from the reaction $\gamma + p \longrightarrow n + \pi^+$ has been measured in several laboratories for photon energies between 160 and 500 MeV. The agreement between the results obtained by different techniques, for example, scintillation counters and photographic emulsions, is, in general, very good. Unfortunately the analysis of the data is complicated by the fact that it is not possible to expand the differential cross-section directly in terms of a power series, as in (5.5). In the case of charged pion photoproduction, the interaction of the photon with the meson current brings in an extra term (p. 54), which is sometimes known as the relativistic term, or the direct interaction term. Before the differential cross-section can be written in terms of a power series, each individual measurement, at a given angle and energy of the pion, must be multiplied by $(1 - \beta\cos\theta)^2$ where $\beta = v/c$ and $v$ is the pion velocity. Then one can write

$$(1 - \beta \cos \theta)^2 \frac{d\sigma}{d\Omega}$$

$$= A + B \cos \theta + C \cos^2 \theta + D \cos^3 \theta + E \cos^4 \theta + \dots \quad (5.6)$$

An analysis of the data between 150 and 470 MeV by Moravscik

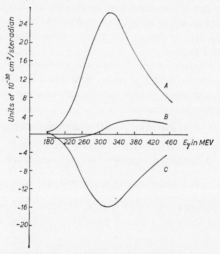

Fig. 18. The coefficients A, B, C of the
angular distribution of the neutral pions from
$\gamma + p \rightarrow p + \pi^0$ as a function of $E\gamma$
(From MCDONALD et al. Phys. Rev. **107**, 577 (1957)

(1957) shows that the five coefficients $A$–$E$ are needed to represent the data. None of the coefficients is simply related to the contributions to the scattering from the different angular momentum states, or different multipole transitions, although $A$ is largely made up of the $s$-wave contribution to the scattering. All the coefficients have a maximum value (either positive or negative) around the position of the $(\frac{3}{2}, \frac{3}{2})$ resonance near to 340 MeV.

## Phenomenological analysis of the experimental data

The production of pions by gamma-rays incident on nucleons is more complicated to analyse than pion–nucleon scattering, since the coupling of the electromagnetic field with mesons and nucleons is more involved than that of mesons alone with nucleons. Much of the analysis of the data has been in terms of a phenomenological model which assumes (a) the existence of a strong interaction in the $T = \frac{3}{2}$, $J = \frac{3}{2}$ state, and (b) that only the two lowest angular momentum states of the pions need be considered. Since the data is to be analysed in terms of angular momentum and isotopic spin, it is necessary first to discuss the angular momentum states of an electromagnetic field.

*Expansion of an electromagnetic wave into multipoles*

The electromagnetic field is a vector field and the electromagnetic waves are vector waves, which can be conveniently expressed* in terms of a potential vector

$$A(r, t) = A_0 \exp [i(kr - \omega t)] + \text{complex conjugate} \quad (5.7)$$

where $A_0 = |A_0| \exp [i\alpha]$ is a complex vector and $|A_0|$ a real vector (the polarization vector). If we normalize and write $A_0 = \dfrac{1}{\sqrt{2}}(\epsilon_x \pm i\epsilon_y)$ where $\epsilon_x$ and $\epsilon_y$ are two real vectors, they must be mutually perpendicular, that is $\epsilon_x . \epsilon_y = 0$ for $|A|^2$ is real. Thus, we can choose the axes $X$ and $Y$ parallel to them and (5.7) can be written

$$A(r, t) = \frac{1}{\sqrt{2}}(\epsilon_x \pm i\epsilon_y) \exp [i(kz - \omega t)] + \text{complex conjugate} \quad (5.8)$$

which represents two circularly polarized waves, where the direction of propagation is along the $Z$-axis. The positive sign corresponds to right circular polarization and the negative sign to left circular polarization, and $\dfrac{1}{\sqrt{2}}(\epsilon_x \pm i\epsilon_y)$ is the circular polarization or spin vector, $S$. For photons $S = 1$; the corresponding spin eigenvalues, $m_s$, are $\pm 1$; $m_s = 0$ is absent because the electromagnetic field is transverse.

The exponential part of (5.8) can be treated as in the usual partial wave analysis and it can be shown† to consist of states of definite

---

* See, for example, Schiff, *Quantum Mechanics*, Ch. X.
† For example, see Bernardini, 1955.

angular momentum and parity, although the primary plane wave (5.7) is neither a definite angular momentum state nor a definite parity state. If we consider the state with orbital angular momentum, $l$, this combines with the spin vector to give $J$ values of $J_\gamma = l, l \pm 1$ where $l = 1, 2, 3 \ldots$ The component of $J$, $m_j$ is equal to $m_s = \pm 1$ always, for $m_l = 0$. This comes about because the flow of energy associated with the electromagnetic field is given by the Poynting Vector $\mathbf{E} \times \mathbf{H}$ and there is therefore also a flow of momentum. Thus for any arbitrary axis there will in general be a finite angular momentum about this axis. However, the energy flow has been taken to be parallel to the $Z$-axis (equations 5.7 and 5.8) and thus the $Z$ component of angular momentum is zero, i.e. $m_l = 0$. Since $m_j = \pm 1$ then $J_\gamma$ cannot be equal to zero.

Now for spin 1 particles there are usually three substates of $l$ for a given $J$ value, namely $J - 1$, $J$ and $J + 1$. However, $m_s = 0$ is forbidden and only the two substates of $l = J$ and $l = J \pm 1$ mixed are allowed. If $l = J_\gamma$ it can be shown that the parity is given by $-(-1)^J$ and this is known as magnetic multipole radiation; if $l = J_\gamma \pm 1$ the parity is $+(-1)^J$ and this is electric multipole radiation.* $J_\gamma = 1$ corresponds to dipole radiation, $J_\gamma = 2$ to quadrupole radiation, and so on. We may state these results in tabular form which shows the notation employed (Table 7).

TABLE 7

| $J_\gamma$ | Terms | | | |
|---|---|---|---|---|
| 0 | never | | — | |
| 1 | Dipole | $J \pm 1 = 0, 2$ odd component | | $E1$ (electric) |
| | | $J = 1$ even | ,, | $M1$ (magnetic) |
| 2 | Quadrupole | $J \pm = 1, 3$ even | ,, | $E2$ (electric) |
| | | $J = 2$ odd | ,, | $M2$ (magnetic) |

The phenomenological analysis of the data has been made on the

* For a full discussion see, for instance, Blatt and Weisskopf, *Theoretical Nuclear Physics* (1952), p. 796 et seq.

assumption that only values of $J_\gamma = 1$ or 2 need be considered. In order to illustrate the terminology, consider the absorption of a photon by a proton, which will spend part of its time as a neutron plus a pion. The incoming photon may catch the system in the latter state and eject the pion. Let us suppose that the photon brings in angular momentum $J_\gamma = 1$ (dipole radiation). The total angular momentum of the initial system of photon plus proton is $\frac{1}{2}$ or $\frac{3}{2}$ ($\frac{1}{2}$ from the nucleon spin and 1 from the $J_\gamma$) and will be of odd parity if the incident dipole radiation is electric dipole. (The nucleon has positive intrinsic parity.) The parity of the final system will also be odd if the pion is emitted into an $s$-state ($l_\pi = 0$), for the pion has negative intrinsic parity. The total angular momentum will be conserved, for in the final state it will be $J = \frac{1}{2}$, that is, only the nucleon spin if $l_\pi = 0$, remembering that $s_\pi = 0$. $J = \frac{3}{2}$ in the final state is not allowed for an electric dipole transition, for then $l_\pi = 1$ and parity would not be conserved.

In the particular transition under discussion, the nucleon spin is reversed or 'flips'. This may be seen from the following argument. The initial proton has spin up, $j_z = +\frac{1}{2}$; the incoming photon transfers a $z$ component of angular momentum equal to $\pm 1$. Thus the final state has $j_z = +\frac{3}{2}$ or $-\frac{1}{2}$, but since $J = \frac{1}{2}$ in the final state the latter is the only possibility. The spin of the nucleon is therefore reversed in the transition.

## Angular distributions for pure states

The production of pions in terms of general angular momentum arguments was first considered by Feld (1953). For photons in pure states, that is electric or magnetic multipoles of given order, these arguments lead to specific angular distributions for the emitted pions. Consider as an example, incident magnetic dipole radiation ($J_\gamma = 1$, $l_\gamma = 1$, parity even). The intermediate state of nucleon + photon has even parity and $J = \frac{1}{2}$ or $\frac{3}{2}$; suppose it is the $\frac{3}{2}$ state. Then the emitted pion must have $l_\pi = 1, 3 \ldots$ in order to conserve parity, but only $l_\pi = 1$ is allowed by conservation of total angular momentum. Now, provided a reaction can be visualized to proceed through states of definite angular momentum and parity, it can be shown that the angular distribution of the reaction is independent of the specific nature of the interaction. For example, in the case discussed above, it is found that

$$\frac{d\sigma}{d\Omega}(\theta) = 2 + 3\sin^2\theta \qquad (5.9)$$

and for an electric quadrupole transition ($E2$)

$$\frac{d\sigma}{d\Omega}(\theta) = 1 + \cos^2\theta \qquad (5.10)$$

Table 8 summarizes the expected angular distributions for given initial and final pure states. In fact, of course, the states are usually

TABLE 8

| $\gamma$-ray pole absorbed | Total $J$ and parity | $l_\pi$ | Spin flipping | Pion angular distribution |
|---|---|---|---|---|
| $E1$ (electric dipole) | $(1/2)-$ $(3/2)-$ | 0 2 | yes yes | constant $2 + 3\sin^2\theta$ |
| $M1$ (magnetic dipole) | $(1/2)+$ $(3/2)+$ | 1 1 | no no | constant $2 + 3\sin^2\theta$ |
| $E2$ (electric quadrupole) | $(3/2)+$ $(5/2)+$ | 1 3 | yes yes | $1 + \cos^2\theta$ $1 + 6\cos^2\theta - 5\cos^4\theta$ |

mixed and the situation is more complex. For example, for an $E1$ transition of amplitude '$a$' to a $S_{\frac{1}{2}}$ final state plus an $M1$ transition of amplitude '$b$' to a $P_{\frac{3}{2}}$ final state then

$$\frac{d\sigma}{d\Omega}(\theta) = |a|^2 + |b|^2(1 + \tfrac{3}{2}\sin^2\theta) + 2Rea^*b\cos\theta \quad (5.11)$$

that is, a $\cos\theta$ term is introduced which gives rise to an asymmetry about 90° in the angular distribution.

### The theory of pion photoproduction

There are three forms of photoproduction of pions from protons.

H

These are:

(i) the proton absorbs the photon and emits a pion, which may be charged or neutral. The Feynman diagrams for this process are shown in Fig. 19. Note that quantum mechanically the proton can

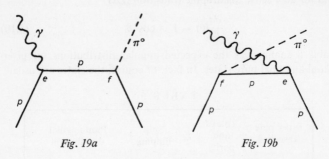

*Fig. 19a*                                    *Fig. 19b*

emit the pion before the photon is absorbed so that both (*a*) and (*b*) are required. This process has been termed the 'shake-off transition' (Marshak, 1952). It is closely connected with pion–nucleon scattering as will be shown later. In terms of the non-relativistic (fixed nucleon) theory, this is the magnetic moment interaction of a photon with a nucleon. The transition involved is the $M1$ transition which we have discussed earlier. It contributes to the resonant state, for $J = \frac{3}{2}$ in the final state, and it is effective for *p*-wave pions only (see Table 8).

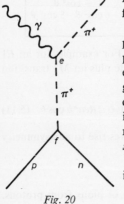

*Fig. 20*

(ii) the photon interacts directly with the pion cloud about the nucleon and ejects a pion. This is known as the 'photoelectric effect' and the corresponding Feynman diagram is shown in Fig. 20. This process is effective only for charged pions as there is no interaction between a photon and a neutral pion, but it will give rise to both *s*- and *p*-wave mesons.

(iii) the pion is produced through the interaction term

$$\bar{\psi}\boldsymbol{\sigma}.\mathbf{A}(\tau_+\phi_- - \tau_-\phi_+)\psi$$

of equation (3.42) discussed earlier on page 54, and which has the diagram, or vertex, shown in Fig. 21. This term arises from the application of the gauge invariance condition to the pseudo-vector pion theory discussed in Chapter III. This is known as the 'catastrophic effect' and is effective only for charged pions. This process gives rise to s-wave pion production, for there are no terms involving the velocity or momentum of the meson.

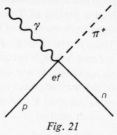

Fig. 21

The more general formulation of these ideas will now be outlined, following in particular the approach adopted by Chew and Low (1956). In this book it is possible only to indicate the origin of the important equations, and to quote them without proof.

The interaction of a photon with a nucleon may be split into two distinct parts. First, consider the interaction of the photon with the magnetic moment of the proton and of the neutron; this is approximately (i) above, and is represented by Fig. 19. As in classical electromagnetic theory the interaction energy is $\mathbf{M}.\mathbf{H}$, where $\mathbf{M}$ is the magnetic moment and $\mathbf{H}$ is the magnetic field associated with the incoming photon. Further

$$\mathbf{H} = \operatorname{curl} \mathbf{A} = \int \mathbf{k} \times A_k \exp{(ikr)} \quad \text{(see 5.7)}$$

and

$$\mathbf{M} = \boldsymbol{\sigma}\mu$$

where $\boldsymbol{\sigma}$ is the nucleon spin, $k$ is the momentum of the incoming photon and $\mu$ is the magnetic moment in Bohr magnetons. For a nucleon, which can be either a proton or a neutron, the interaction energy can be written as

$$(\boldsymbol{\sigma}.\mathbf{H})\mu_p(\tfrac{1}{2} + \tau_3) + (\boldsymbol{\sigma}.\mathbf{H})\mu_n(\tfrac{1}{2} - \tau_3)$$

where the subscripts $p$ and $n$ refer to proton and neutron respectively, and $\tau_3 = +\tfrac{1}{2}$ for a proton and $-\tfrac{1}{2}$ for a neutron. Rearranging the above expression yields for the interaction energy

$$\tfrac{1}{2}(\boldsymbol{\sigma}.\mathbf{H})(\mu_p + \mu_n) + \tfrac{1}{2}(\boldsymbol{\sigma}.\mathbf{H})\tau_3(\mu_p - \mu_n) \tag{5.12}$$

The first term has no isotopic spin dependence and is therefore known as an isotopic scalar. It will lead a proton (say) with $T = \frac{1}{2}$, $J = \frac{1}{2}$ (its spin) into a state of $T = \frac{1}{2}$ and total angular momentum of $\frac{1}{2}$ or $\frac{3}{2}$ for the photon brings in angular momentum 1. The second term contains the vector $\tau_3$ and is therefore an isotopic vector. It can lead a proton of $T = \frac{1}{2}$, $J = \frac{1}{2}$ into a state with $T = \frac{3}{2}$, and total angular momentum of $\frac{3}{2}$ for the $\tau_3$ enables the $T$ value to be changed. Thus if the $T = \frac{3}{2}$, $J = \frac{3}{2}$ resonance dominates the production process, which is certainly true for neutral pions, the first term may be neglected; in any case $\mu_p + \mu_n \sim 0$. Now from the point of view of the mathematical manipulations involved, the incoming photon, of momentum $\mathbf{k}$ and polarization vector $\boldsymbol{\epsilon}$, may be replaced by an incident neutral pion of momentum $\mathbf{p}$ defined by

$$\frac{\mathbf{p}}{p} = \frac{\mathbf{k} \times \boldsymbol{\epsilon}}{|\mathbf{k} \times \boldsymbol{\epsilon}|} \quad \text{and} \quad |p| = |k| \quad \text{so that} \quad \mathbf{p} = k \cdot \frac{\mathbf{k} \times \boldsymbol{\epsilon}}{|\mathbf{k} \times \boldsymbol{\epsilon}|}$$

This substitution is accompanied by certain kinematical factors to allow for the finite rest mass of the pion. The problem is then that of the scattering of a neutral pion by a nucleon, and Chew and Low argue that the total cross-section for the production of $p$-wave neutral pions $\sigma_{TP}^{\gamma 0}$ may be written as

$$\sigma_{TP}^{\gamma 0} = \frac{C}{4\pi} \cdot \frac{1}{f^2} \cdot \frac{1}{v_\pi{}^2} \left( \frac{\mu_p - \mu_n}{2} \right)^2 \mid T_{q0}(q) \mid^2 \tag{5.13}$$

where $\mid T_{q0}(q) \mid$ is the scattering amplitude for the scattering of $p$-wave neutral pions by protons, and which is related to the corresponding total cross-section $\sigma_{TP}^{00}$ by

$$\sigma_{TP}^{00} = \frac{C}{4\pi} \mid T_{q0}(q) \mid^2 \tag{5.14}$$

In these equations $v_\pi = q_0/\omega_q$ is the velocity of the pion of momentum $q_0$ and total energy $\omega_q$, $f^2$ is the coupling constant, and $C \simeq q\omega_q/(2\pi)^2 \left(1 + \frac{\omega}{M}\right)^2$ where $M$ is the nucleon rest mass. An expression similar to (5.13) may be written down for $p$-wave charged pion production through the $T = \frac{3}{2}$, $J = \frac{3}{2}$ resonant state.

The second interaction is that of the incident photon with the meson cloud or current around the nucleon. This is only operative, of course, for the case of charged pions. It can be argued that the resultant scattering amplitude is given approximately by Born approximation, which yields an expression of the form

$$\pm \frac{\sqrt{2}\,ief\pi}{(\omega_q k)^{\frac{1}{2}}}\left\{\sigma.\epsilon - \frac{2[\sigma(\mathbf{q}-\mathbf{k})](\mathbf{q}.\epsilon)}{(\mathbf{k}-\mathbf{q})^2 - (k_0-q_0)^2 + m_\pi^2}\right\} \qquad (5.15)$$

where $m_\pi$ is the pion rest mass and $e$ is the elementary electronic charge. The presence of the term

$$\{(\mathbf{k}-\mathbf{q})^2 - (k_0-q_0)^2 + m_\pi^2\} =$$
$$2\,(k_0 q_0 - \mathbf{k}.\mathbf{q}) = 2\,q_0\,|\,\mathbf{k}\,|\,(1-\beta\cos\theta)$$

where $\beta = |\,q_1/q_0$ is an important factor which has to be allowed for in the form of the angular distribution for charged pion production (see p. 92). Another important feature of this part of the scattering is that at threshold only the term $\sigma.\epsilon$ survives, while (5.13) also vanishes. Thus the scattering amplitude at zero energy has the form

$$\pm \frac{\sqrt{2}\,ief\pi}{(\omega_q k)^{\frac{1}{2}}}\sigma.\epsilon \qquad (5.16)$$

All the terms in this equation are numerical factors, which can be calculated so that the coupling constant $f$ can be unambiguously determined. In fact, this relation may be used as a definition of $f$, as proposed by Kroll and Ruderman (1954).

Expression (5.15) above includes both processes (ii) and (iii) mentioned on pages 98–99. The catastrophic effect is given by the term in $\sigma.\epsilon$ for $A_k(r) = \frac{1}{\sqrt{2k}}\epsilon.e^{ikr}$ so that it is proportional to $\frac{ief}{\sqrt{\omega_q}}\sigma.A$, together with the $\tau$ and $\phi$ factors which have been omitted in (5.15). This interaction produces $s$-wave pions only. The second term in the brackets (5.15) corresponds to the photoelectric effect (process (ii)) and is zero near threshold.

These results have been obtained on the assumptions listed on page 80 in Chapter IV. A more refined treatment is given by the use of relativistic dispersion theory (Chew et al., 1957) which allows recoil corrections to be made in the formulae relating photoproduction to scattering. A comparison between the experimental values of the coefficients $A$ to $E$ of (5.6), and those predicted from both the

Chew–Low theory and the dispersion relations, has been given by Moravcsik (1957). Except at energies above 400 MeV the predictions of these two forms of the theory are almost identical.

## Comparison of the experimental data with theory

### (a) Neutral pion production

The predominant process for the production of neutral pions is the magnetic moment interaction of (5.13), which corresponds to a magnetic dipole transition. The expected variation with energy of the total cross-section for this process can be calculated from (5.13) provided $\sigma_{TP}^{00}$ is known. This can be obtained as the difference between the total cross-section for the direct scattering of neutral pions by protons, $\sigma^{00}$, and the total cross-section for the direct scattering of $s$-wave neutral pions by protons. It is readily shown, following the approach adopted on page 57, that, in terms of scattering amplitudes

$$\sigma^{00} = \tfrac{4}{9} \, |\, a(\tfrac{3}{2})\,|^2 + \tfrac{1}{9} \, |\, a(\tfrac{1}{2})\,|^2$$

These amplitudes may be expressed in terms of the total cross-sections for processes (4.1) to (4.3), which may be written as $\sigma^{++}$, $\sigma^{--}$ and $\sigma^{-0}$. It turns out that

$$2\sigma^{00} = \sigma^{++} + \sigma^{--} + \sigma^{-0} \tag{5.17}$$

The cross-section for the $s$-wave part of the neutral pion scattering can be shown to be

$$\sigma_{TS}^{00} = \frac{4\pi\lambda^2}{9} \Big\{ 6 \sin^2 \delta_3 + 3 \sin^2\delta_1 - 2 \sin^2 (\delta_1 - \delta_3) \Big\} \tag{5.18}$$

All the quantities in (5.17) and (5.18) have been determined so that $\sigma_{TP}^{00}$, as a function of energy, can be calculated. From (5.13) and (5.14) one can write

$$\frac{\sigma_{TP}^{\gamma 0}}{\sigma_{TP}^{00}} = \frac{(\mu_p - \mu_n)^2}{16\pi f^2 v_\pi} = \frac{0\cdot0026}{v_\pi} \quad \text{for } f^2 = 0\cdot081$$

or

$$\sigma_{TP}^{\gamma 0} = 0\cdot0026\,\sigma_{TP}^{00}/v_\pi \tag{5.19}$$

The full line in Fig. 22 is a plot of $\sigma_{TP}^{\gamma 0}$ derived from this relation, while the points are experimental determinations of the *total* cross-section for neutral pion photoproduction from protons. The close agreement between the curve and the points not only demonstrates the relationship between photoproduction and scattering, expressed by (5.19), but shows that the $s$-wave photoproduction of neutral pions is small, at least up to $E_\gamma$ of 350 MeV. ($E_\gamma = T_{\pi^+} + 150\cdot1$ MeV

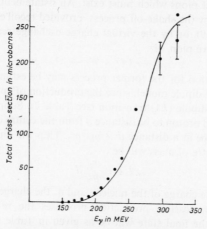

*Fig. 22. The total cross-section for neutral pion production as a function of $E_y$. The circles are experimental points while the full line is calculated using the pion–nucleon scattering phase shifts*

(From KOESTER and MILLS. *Phys. Rev.* **105**, 1900 (1957))

where $T_{\pi^+}$ is the kinetic energy of the incident $\pi^+$ mesons in the scattering data.)

Any $s$-wave contribution to the production process will be detectable mainly through its interference effects. If only $p$-wave emission occurs, and if we consider only magnetic dipole transitions (that is, neglecting $E2$ transitions), then the angular distribution will be of the form

$$\frac{d\sigma}{d\Omega} = 2 + 3\sin^2\theta = 5 - 3\cos^2\theta \qquad (5.9)$$

Thus in terms of (5.5) $A/C = 5/3$ with $B$ zero. The experimental data of McDonald *et al.* (1957) yields $1\cdot60 \pm 0\cdot10$ for the average value of $A/C$ over the energy range 260–450 MeV, but $B$ is found to be finite, although small, above about 280 MeV (see Fig. 18). $B$ is an interference term, so that a finite value for it indicates some $s$-wave production at the higher energies. There are, in fact, two sources of $s$-wave neutral pions which must exist. An $s$-state neutral pion can be produced by the shake-off process, provided recoil effects are included (Fig. 19), or by the virtual charge exchange scattering of a created positive pion, viz.

$$\gamma + p \longrightarrow (\pi^+ + n) \longrightarrow \pi^0 + p \tag{5.20}$$

The cross-section for the former process may be estimated using a simple electric dipole model, since the production of an $s$-wave pion is an electric dipole ($E1$) transition (see Table 7). Suppose we consider the recoil proton to be distance $d$ from the centre of mass, then the pion will be at a distance $d \times m_p/m_\pi$. Thus the dipole moment about the centre of mass will be

$$e_n d + e_\pi \frac{m_p}{m_\pi}.d$$

where $e_n$ is the charge of the nucleon and $e_\pi$ the charge of the pion. For the four possible production processes the relative dipole moments in the final state will be as given in Table 9. We might expect that the scattering amplitudes for $E1$ transitions, yielding $s$-wave pions, would be proportional to these dipole moments. This is so, provided we put in charge independence. The initial nucleon

TABLE 9

| Process | Dipole moment | Relative dipole moment | Relative cross-section |
|---------|---------------|------------------------|------------------------|
| $\gamma + p \longrightarrow n + \pi^+$ | $\dfrac{M}{m_\pi}.d$ | $\dfrac{M}{m_\pi}$ | $1$ |
| $\gamma + p \longrightarrow p + \pi^0$ | $d$ | $1$ | $\frac{1}{2}\left(\dfrac{m_\pi}{M}\right)^2$ |
| $\gamma + n \longrightarrow n + \pi^0$ | $0$ | $0$ | $0$ |
| $\gamma + n \longrightarrow p + \pi^-$ | $d + \dfrac{M}{m_\pi}.d$ | $1 + \dfrac{M}{m_\pi}$ | $\left(1 + \dfrac{m_\pi}{M}\right)^2$ |

system has $T = \frac{1}{2}$, and equations (3.18) and (3.19) show that the scattering amplitude for $\gamma + p \longrightarrow n + \pi^+$ is $\sqrt{2}$ times that for $\gamma + p \longrightarrow p + \pi^0$, and similarly for the $\gamma + n$ reactions. The expressions for the relative cross-sections, given in the last column of Table 9, have been obtained by multiplying the dipole moments by the appropriate normalization factors and then squaring and rearranging. On the basis of this argument only about 1% of the $\gamma + p$ reactions will lead to $s$-wave neutral pions compared to $s$-wave positive pions. The second source of $s$-wave neutral pions, the virtual charge exchange process (5.20), may be regarded as a combination of the processes represented by Fig. 21 and Fig. 19. Detailed calculation shows that the yield of neutral mesons in this way is very small.

### (b) Charged pion production

Near threshold the dominant production process is that of the $s$-wave emission of pions through the catastrophic effect. It has already been mentioned that the cross-section at threshold gives, in principle, a direct determination of the coupling constant. For example, Beneventano et al. (1956) found $f^2 \cong 0.073$. The extrapolation procedures employed have been the subject of some discussion (see p. 72 and also Puppi (1958)), but the experimental data appear to be consistent with $f^2 \cong 0.08$. This is in satisfactory agreement with that obtained from the analysis of pion–nucleon scattering experiments. The cross-sections for pion production near threshold, through processes (i) and (ii) listed on page 98, have been shown to be very small.

At energies well above threshold the $p$-wave emission of pions becomes important, both through the second term of (5.15) (photoelectric effect), and through a term similar to (5.13) but containing the scattering cross-sections for charged pions. The latter contains contributions from the $(\frac{3}{2}, \frac{3}{2})$ resonant state. If charged pion production took place only through this state, then the branching ratio of positive to neutral pion production is determined by charge independence. In terms of isotopic spin wave functions

$$u_n \pi^+ = -\sqrt{\tfrac{1}{3}}\Psi(\tfrac{3}{2}, +\tfrac{1}{2}) + \sqrt{\tfrac{2}{3}}\Psi(\tfrac{1}{2}, +\tfrac{1}{2})$$

and
$$u_p \pi^0 = \sqrt{\tfrac{2}{3}}\Psi(\tfrac{3}{2}, +\tfrac{1}{2}) + \sqrt{\tfrac{1}{3}}\Psi(\tfrac{1}{2}, +\tfrac{1}{2}) \qquad (3.24)$$

If pion production took place only through the $T = \frac{3}{2}$ state, the total cross-section for $\pi^+$ production would be one-half of that for $\pi^0$ production. Further, the neutral pions are known to be produced predominantly from the $T = \frac{3}{2}$ state. Thus the approximate equality of the $\pi^+$ and $\pi^0$ production cross-sections near the resonance energy shows that about one-half of the $\pi^+$ production must take place through $s$-wave, and non-resonant $p$-wave, interactions.

## BIBLIOGRAPHY

BERNARDINI, G. 1955. *Nuovo Cimento*, **II**, Supplemento No. 1, 104–38 (Lectures at Varenna in 1954).

BETHE, H. A. and HOFFMANN, F. DE. 1955. *Mesons and Fields*, **II.** *Mesons*. Section 35, 36, 37.

CHEW, G. F. 1959. *Handbuch der Physik*, **43.** Springer (theory).

DALITZ, R. H. 1955. *Progress in Nuclear Physics*, **4**, 95.

FERMI, E. 1955. *Nuovo Cimento*, **II**, Supplemento No. 1, 45–63 (Lectures at Varenna in 1954).

GELL-MANN, M. and WATSON, K. M. 1954. *Ann. Rev. Nuc. Sci.* **4**, 219.

## REFERENCES

BENEVENTANO, M., STOPPINI, G., TAU, L. and BERNARDINI, G. 1956. *CERN Symposium*, **II**, 259.

BERNARDINI, G. and GOLDWASSER, E. L. 1954a. *Phys. Rev.* **94**, 729; 1954b. ibid. **95**, 857.

CHEW, G. F., GOLDBERGER, M. L., LOW, F. E. and NAMBU, Y. 1957. *Phys. Rev.* **106**, 1345.

CHEW, G. F. and LOW, F. E. 1956. *Phys. Rev.* **101**, 1579.

FELD, B. 1953. *Phys. Rev.* **89**, 330.

GOLDSCHMIDT-CLERMONT, Y., OSBORNE, L. S. and SCOTT, M. 1953. *Phys. Rev.* **89**, 329; 1955. ibid. **97**, 188.

KOESTER, L. J. and MILLS, F. E. 1957. *Phys. Rev.* **105**, 1900.

KROLL, N. M. and RUDERMAN, M. A. 1954. *Phys. Rev.* **93**, 233.

MARSHAK, R. E. 1952. *Meson Physics*, 7–8. McGraw-Hill.

MCDONALD, W. S., PETERSON, V. Z. and CORSON, D. R. 1957. *Phys. Rev.* **107**, 577.

MORAVSCIK, M. J. 1956. *Phys. Rev.* **104**, 1451; 1957. ibid. **107**, 600.

OAKLEY, D. C. and WALKER, R. L. 1955. *Phys. Rev.* **97**, 1283.

PUPPI, G. 1958. *CERN Conference on High Energy Physics*, 39.

TOLLESTRUP, A. V., KECK, J. C. and WORLOCK, R. M. 1955. *Phys. Rev.* **99**, 220.

WALKER, R. L., OAKLEY, D. C. and TOLLESTRUP, A. V. 1955. *Phys. Rev.* **97**, 1279.

# CHAPTER VI

# Nucleon–Nucleus Scattering

## Introduction

The first studies of the disintegration of a nucleus by a fast nucleon were carried out as long ago as 1937 by Blau and Wambacher. These workers observed nuclear disintegrations in photographic emulsions which had been exposed to the cosmic radiation at mountain altitudes. Since that time much work has been carried out on the analysis and interpretation of such events, and the general picture of the different phenomena that occur is now clear. We shall not discuss this aspect of nucleon–nucleus interactions in this book; for a detailed survey of this subject reference may be made to the review article of Camerini *et al.* (1952). Here we shall be concerned with the representation of nucleon–nucleus scattering in terms of the fundamental cross-sections for scattering or for absorption. In particular, the optical model of the nucleus will be described in some detail.

When a nucleus is struck by an incident nucleon there are two basic interactions that can occur. The incident nucleon may be scattered by the nucleus without transferring energy to it other than that required to conserve energy and momentum; this is elastic scattering. On the other hand the incident nucleon may interact with the target nucleus, transfer energy to it, and change the internal structure of the nucleus; this is absorption. The sum of the cross-sections for the elastic scattering and for the absorption (or reaction) processes is known as the total cross-section.

We may derive expressions for the cross-sections for the elastic scattering, $\sigma_e$, and the absorption, $\sigma_a$, by making use of the partial wave analysis given in Chapter III. It was shown there that for scattering by a central potential the asymptotic form of the wave function may be written as

$$\psi \sim \sum_l \frac{(2l+1)i^l \, P_l(\cos\theta)}{kr} \frac{1}{2i} \left[ S_l e^{i(kr-l\pi/2)} - e^{-i(kr-l\pi/2)} \right]$$

(3.28) and (3.29)

where the first term in the square bracket represents an outgoing spherical wave and the second term an incoming spherical wave. The incident plane wave is represented by the incoming spherical wave plus part of the outgoing spherical wave, the remainder being the scattered wave, so that the above equation may be written as

$$\psi \sim \sum_l \frac{(2l+1)i^l}{kr} \frac{P_l(\cos\theta)}{2i}$$
$$\times \left[ e^{i(kr-l\pi/2)} - e^{i(kr-l\pi/2)} + S_l - e^{i(kr-l\pi/2)} - e^{+i(kr-l\pi/2)} \right] \quad (6.1)$$

The first two terms now represent the incident plane wave (see 3.31). For a real potential there is no absorption and the flux in must equal the flux of particles going out. The flux in may be taken as unity and the flux out as equal to $|S_l|^2 = 1$ therefore. It is thus convenient to write $S_l = e^{2i\delta_l}$ where $\delta_l$, the phase shift, is real.

If there are also absorptive reactions occurring, these may be represented by taking the potential to be complex. In this case the flux in the outgoing wave is less than that in the ingoing wave, i.e. $|S_l|^2 < 1$. In terms of the phase shift $\delta_l$ this means that the phase shift becomes complex, with a positive imaginary part.

The total elastic scattering cross-section is given by

$$\sigma_e = \text{flux of the outgoing wave of (6.1)}$$
$$= \sum_l \frac{\pi}{k^2}(2l+1) \, | \, S_l - 1 \, |^2 \quad (6.2)$$

obtained by integrating the square of the outgoing flux over all angles (see pp. 43–44). The absorption cross-section is given by computing the difference between the outgoing flux and the ingoing flux, with the result

$$\sigma_a = \sum_l \frac{\pi}{k^2}(2l+1)(1 - | \, S_l \, |^2) \quad (6.3)$$

It is important to note that the presence of absorption (some $|S_l| < 1$) necessarily requires a corresponding elastic scattering (since $(S_l - 1)$ is then non-zero) whereas the converse is not true (that is, $(S_l - 1)$ may be non-vanishing even though $|S_l| = 1$).

The total cross-section, $\sigma_t$, is given by

$$\sigma_t = \sigma_a + \sigma_e = \frac{\pi}{k^2} \sum_l (2l + 1)(2 - S_l - S_l^*)$$

Now the scattering amplitude at an angle $\theta$, $f(\theta)$, is

$$f(\theta) = \sum_l \frac{(2l + 1)}{2ik} P_l(\cos \theta)\{S_l - 1\} \quad \text{(see p. 43)}$$

so that for $\theta = 0^0$

$$f(0) = \frac{1}{2ik} \sum_l (2l + 1)(S_l - 1)$$

In terms of the phase shifts, $\delta_l$, where $S_l = e^{2i\delta_l}$ it is readily shown that

$$Im f(0) = \frac{1}{k} \sum_l (2l + 1) \sin^2 \delta_l$$

But in the expression given above for $\sigma_t$,

$$2 - S_l - S_l^* = 2 - 2Re S_l = 4 \sin^2 \delta_l$$

and substituting for $\sin^2 \delta_l$ in the expression for $Im f(0)$ we obtain

$$\sigma_t = \frac{4\pi}{k} Im f(0) \tag{6.4}$$

as a general result.

The preceding discussion ignores the presence of nucleon spin and also the possibility that the target nucleus has a net spin, so that the spin-orbit forces are specifically excluded.

### The optical model

It was first pointed out by Serber (1947) that a nucleus will appear partially transparent to high-energy nucleons ($\sim$100 MeV), for the mean free path of such a nucleon within nuclear matter is then comparable to the nuclear radius. Thus it is natural to draw the optical analogy of the scattering of light by a partially opaque sphere. The nucleus may be regarded as a sphere of radius $R = r_0 A^{\frac{1}{3}}$ where $r_0$ is a constant and equal to about $1 \cdot 2 \times 10^{-13}$ cm. This is equivalent to assuming that the nuclear density, $\rho$, of nuclear matter is constant, with the value

$$\rho = \frac{A}{\frac{4}{3}\pi R^3} = \frac{3}{4\pi r_0{}^3}$$

If a nucleus is placed in the path of an incoming wave of particles, three different wave phenomena can occur: (i) reflection at the surface, (ii) refraction in passing through the nucleus, and (iii) diffraction round the nucleus (see Fig. 23). All these effects are elastic since

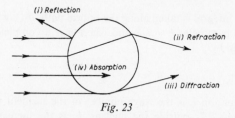

*Fig. 23*

they involve no energy loss by the incident particle, and they are coherent (that is, the strength of the total scattered wave is to be obtained from the sum of the three amplitudes for these scattered waves). Processes (i) and (ii) are included in a quantum mechanical treatment (for the case where there is no diffraction) if the nucleus is represented by a real potential well. If some of the incident particles are absorbed by the nucleus (process (iv)), this inelastic absorptive process may be included in the description of the scattering by adding an imaginary part to the potential. The diffraction scattering then follows as a necessary consequence of the absorption of the incident wave, due to the absorptive processes (iv) represented by the imaginary part of the potential, as we have shown in the previous section. Now, the assumption of a sharp edge to the nucleus (or potential) is physically unreasonable and must be replaced by the assumption of a diffuse edge (that is the potential distribution, as a function of distance, is tapered in shape). This means that the surface reflection of nucleons by the nucleus (process (i)) is negligible. Thus the potential equivalent of the wave phenomena (ii) to (iv) is that of a complex potential $V + iW$, the real part $V$ giving rise to refraction and the imaginary part $iW$, (where $W$ is real) giving rise to absorption and diffraction. The representation of the nucleus by a complex potential is loosely known as the 'optical model'. For any such potential one solves the Schrödinger equation for each value of the angular momentum $l$, and determines the amplitudes $S_l$. In the high-energy limit, where many $l$ waves are involved in the collision, the formulae for $\sigma_s$ and $\sigma_a$ take on the forms characteristic of the model in this limit, where summation over the different $l$ values may be replaced by integrals. In this case $S_l$ is evaluated as $\exp ik \int n.ds$

where the integral is taken along the optical path, $ds$, corresponding to impact parameter $b = l/k$ and where $n$ is a complex refractive index given by

$$n = \frac{k + k_1 + iK/2}{k} \tag{6.5}$$

In this equation $k$ is the wave number of the incident particle, of kinetic energy $T$, outside the nucleus, $k_1$ is the increase in wave number when the particle is inside the nucleus, and $K$ is the absorption coefficient, equal to the reciprocal of the mean free path against collision, $\lambda$. $K$ may be expressed in terms of the free nucleon-nucleon total scattering cross-sections $\sigma_{np}$ and $\sigma_{pp} = \sigma_{nn}$. For example, for neutrons incident on a nucleus of charge $Z$, atomic number $A$, and radius $R$

$$\frac{1}{\lambda} = K = \frac{3A}{4\pi R^3} \cdot \frac{\alpha}{A} [Z\sigma_{np} + (A - Z)\sigma_{nn}] \tag{6.6}$$

$\alpha$ is a numerical factor less than unity, which allows for the fact that the Pauli exclusion principle will forbid some reactions at low energies, thus decreasing $1/\lambda$. At energies of the order of several hundred MeV $\alpha \simeq 1$.

Equation (6.5) may be re-written

$$n = \{(T + V + iW)/T\}^{\frac{1}{2}}$$

or

$$\left(k_1 + \frac{iK}{2}\right)/k = \left(1 + \frac{V + iW}{T}\right)^{\frac{1}{2}} - 1 \tag{6.7}$$

by using the non-relativistic approximation that $\hbar k = p = \sqrt{2mT}$. Expanding (6.7) and equating real and imaginary parts, we have, to a first approximation when $T$ is large compared to $V$

$$\frac{k_1}{k} = \frac{V}{2T} \quad \text{and} \quad \frac{K}{k} = \frac{W}{T} \tag{6.8}$$

At energies of the order of several hundred MeV the correct relativistic relations must be used, in which case the equations corresponding to (6.8) are then

$$k_1 = \frac{E}{k}V \quad \text{and} \quad K = \frac{2E}{k}W \tag{6.9}$$

It is usually assumed that the nucleon, or potential, distribution follows the charge distribution known from the electron scattering experiments of Hofstadter (1956) so that (6.9) becomes

$$k_1 = \frac{E}{k} \int_0^\infty V(r)\, dr \quad \text{and} \quad K = \frac{2E}{k} \int_0^\infty W(r)\, dr \tag{6.10}$$

A further complication must now be introduced. Recent experiments, which will be discussed later in this chapter, have shown that to explain the observed phenomenon of the polarization of proton beams it is necessary to introduce a spin-orbit potential. By this we mean a potential which arises from the coupling between the spin $\boldsymbol{\sigma}$ of the incident nucleon and its orbital angular momentum $\mathbf{L}$ about the target nucleus. Thus the expression for the potential experienced by the incident nucleon (omitting the Coulomb potential) is

$$V = V_c(r) + \boldsymbol{\sigma}.\mathbf{L}\, V_s(r) \tag{6.11}$$

where $\boldsymbol{\sigma}$ and $\mathbf{L}$ are operators, $V_c$ is the complex central potential and $V_s$ is the effective spin-orbit potential, which may also be complex. Thus the six parameters of the complex potential model are the real and imaginary parts of the central potential and of the spin-orbit potential, the form of the potential distribution and the radius of the nucleus. It has been usual to take the last two quantities as being given by the electron scattering data, and to use the nucleon scattering data to find the potentials.

In the next section expressions will be derived for the absorption and elastic scattering cross-sections, on the basis of the simple model of a square well complex potential (Fernbach *et al.*, 1949). The

I

discussion will be specifically for high energies, that is above 100 MeV incident nucleon kinetic energy, and the effect of the Pauli exclusion principle will be ignored. The derivations serve to illustrate the method of approach to the problem. The expressions corresponding to the complete potential of (6.11), with a radial dependence, only will be quoted (e.g. Malenka, 1954; Brown, 1957).

### Derivation of the individual cross-sections

#### (a) Absorption cross-section

Consider first an absorbing disc of radius $R$ and thickness $L$. It is supposed that there is a boundary layer, in which $k_1$ and $K$ rise to their values inside the disc, in a distance larger than $1/k$. There will then be no reflection at the surface, and for unit amplitude of the incident wave, the wave transmitted through the disc will have an amplitude and relative phase, after emerging from the disc, of

$$a = \exp\left(-\frac{K}{2} + ik_1\right)L \qquad (6.12)$$

The absorption cross-section is just $\pi R^2$ times the probability that the incident nucleon strikes a particle in the nucleus, viz.

$$\sigma_a = \pi R^2(1 - |a|^2) = \pi R^2(1 - e^{-KL}) \qquad (6.13)$$

For a sphere of radius $R$, let a wave strike it at a distance $b$ from the centre and emerge after travelling a distance $2s$ (Fig. 24), so that

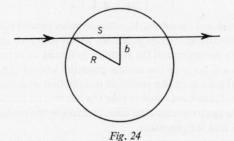

*Fig. 24*

$s^2 = R^2 - b^2$ where $b$ is known as the impact parameter. Its amplitude on emerging is $a = \exp(-K + 2ik_1)s$ so that in place of

(6.13) we have

$$\sigma_a = 2\pi \int_0^R (1 - e^{-2Ks})b\, db = 2\pi \int_R^0 (1 - e^{-2Ks})s\, ds$$

$$= 2\pi \left[ \frac{s^2}{2} + \frac{se^{-2Ks}}{2K} + \frac{e^{-2Ks}}{(2K)^2} \right]_R^0$$

$$\sigma_a = \pi R^2 \left[ 1 - \frac{\{1 - (1 + 2KR)e^{-2KR}\}}{2K^2 R^2} \right] \qquad (6.14)$$

Thus, the absorption cross-section is defined in terms of $R$ and the absorption coefficient $K$ alone.

The general expression is

$$\sigma_a = 2\pi \int_0^\infty [1 - \tfrac{1}{2} \{ \mid \exp (i\chi_1 + i\chi_2) \mid^2 +$$

$$\mid \exp (i\chi_1 - i\chi_2) \mid^2 \}]b\, db \qquad (6.15)$$

and if the spin-orbit potential is completely real this reduces to

$$\sigma_a = 2\pi \int_0^\infty \{1 - \exp (- 2i\chi_1)\}b\, db \qquad (6.16)$$

where

$$\chi_1 = - \frac{E}{k} \int_{-\infty}^{+\infty} V_c\, dz \qquad (6.17)$$

and

$$\chi_2 = - \frac{E}{k} kb \int_{-\infty}^{+\infty} V_s\, dz \qquad (6.18)$$

where $z$ is the coordinate along the beam direction. The system of units in which $\hbar = c = 1$ has been used in these equations.

(b) *Elastic cross-section*

The diffraction or elastic scattering cross-section in the case of a disc is given by the fact that on a plane behind the disc the incident wave is no longer plane, but differs from a plane wave by an amplitude $1 - a$ in the shadow of the disc. This amplitude represents a scattered wave and the corresponding cross-section is

$$\sigma_e = \pi R^2 \mid 1 - a \mid^2$$

$$\therefore \sigma_e = \pi R^2 (1 - 2e^{-(KL/2)} \cos k_1 L + e^{-KL}) \qquad (6.19)$$

For the case of a sphere the corresponding expression is complicated and will not be given here. Expressions for $\sigma_a$ and $\sigma_e$ have been computed for this case (with neglect of the spin-orbit potential) by Bethe and Wilson (1951), who have given a convenient plot of $\sigma_a$ against $\sigma_e$ for various values of $k_1/K$. The angular distribution of the elastic scattering is also of interest. In terms of the high-energy model discussed just above, the scattering amplitude at angle $\theta$ is given by

$$f(\theta) = ik \int_0^R J_0(kb \sin \theta)(e^{i\chi_1} - 1)b\, db$$

where the spin-orbit potential is neglected (Brown, 1957). Considering for simplicity, the case of a black sphere, the phase angle $\chi_1$ is purely imaginary and infinite so that $e^{i\chi_1}$ is zero. In this case the angular distribution simplifies to

$$\frac{d\sigma}{d\Omega} = |f(\theta)|^2 = k^2 \left| \int_0^R J_0(kb \sin \theta)b\, db \right|^2$$

where $J_0$ is a Bessel function of order zero. Now $zJ_0(z) = \dfrac{d}{dz}zJ_1(z)$

where $z$ is any function and $J_1$ is a first-order Bessel function

$$\therefore \frac{d\sigma}{d\Omega} = k^2 \left| \int_0^R \frac{J_0(kb \sin \theta)(kb \sin \theta)d(kb \sin \theta)}{k^2 \sin^2 \theta} \right|^2$$

$$= \frac{1}{k^2 \sin^4 \theta} \left| kR \sin \theta\, J_1(kR \sin \theta) \right|^2 = \left| R\frac{J_1(kR \sin \theta)}{\sin \theta} \right|^2$$

For a black disc $\sigma_e = \pi R^2$ so that

$$\frac{d\sigma}{d\Omega} = \frac{\sigma_e}{\pi} \left[ J_1\frac{(kR \sin \theta)}{\sin \theta} \right]^2 \tag{6.20}$$

The behaviour of this function is shown in Fig. 25. (6.20) can also be derived from the partial wave formula (3.33):

$$\frac{d\sigma}{d\Omega} = \frac{1}{k^2} \left| \sum_l (l + \tfrac{1}{2})(e^{2i\delta_1} - 1)P_l(\cos \theta) \right|^2 \tag{3.33}$$

In the high-energy limit many $l$-waves are involved in the collision and the summation sign can be replaced by an integral over the impact parameter $b$ which is defined as $kb = l + \frac{1}{2}$. Then

$$k \, db = dl \quad \text{and} \quad \frac{d\sigma}{d\Omega} = \frac{1}{k^2} \left| \int_0^R kb(e^{2i\delta_l} - 1)P \, (\cos \theta)k \, db \right|^2$$

where $R$ is the radius of the nucleus. For small values of $\theta$

$$P_l(\cos \theta) = J_0\{(l + \tfrac{1}{2}) \sin \theta\} = J_1(kb \sin \theta)$$

For a 'black' sphere $\delta_l$ is imaginary, so $e^{i\delta_l}$ tends to zero, and the expression for $\frac{d\sigma}{d\Omega}$ then has the same form as that given at the beginning of the previous derivation.

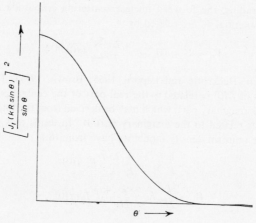

*Fig. 25*

## (c) Total cross-section

The general expression for the total cross-section, $\sigma_t$, is

$$\sigma_t = 4\pi \int_0^\infty [1 - \exp\{-\operatorname{Re}\chi_1\}\cos\{-\operatorname{Im}\chi_1\}\cos\{\chi_2\}]b \, db \quad (6.21)$$

where $\chi_1$ and $\chi_2$ have been defined previously [(6.17) and (6.18)] and $\hbar = c = 1$.

Suppose that we regard the incident nucleon as passing through the nucleus and being scattered by the individual nucleons. This picture is certainly true at high energies, where the wavelength of the incident particle is small compared with the nuclear radius. The scattering amplitudes from all the nucleons in the nucleus may be added and if multiple scattering in the nucleus is neglected we can write

$$f_n(0) = \sum_i \overline{f_i(0)}$$

where $f_i$ is the component of the $i^{th}$ nucleon–nucleon scattering amplitude and the bar indicates that an average over spin and charge states has been carried out. In the approximation in which the range of nucleon–nucleon forces is neglected compared to the nuclear radius, the forward nuclear scattering amplitude and the central potential $V_c$ are related by

$$V_c = V + iW = -\frac{2\pi}{E} \sum_i \overline{f_i(0)} \, \rho(r) \tag{6.22}$$

(Fernbach, Heckrotte and Lepore, 1955; Brown, 1957). Thus the real part of $f_n(0)$ is related to the real part of the central potential, while the imaginary part, which may be derived from the total cross-section, is related to the imaginary part $W$. In terms of $k_1$, $K$ and using the uniform density model we have from (6.11)

$$V = \frac{k}{E}.k_1 = \frac{k}{E}.\frac{2\pi\rho}{k}.R\rho \overline{f(0)} \tag{6.23}$$

and

$$W = \frac{k}{2E}.K = \frac{k}{2E}.\frac{4\pi\rho}{k} \, Im \overline{f(0)} \tag{6.24}$$

## Experimental techniques

The experimental problem is to measure the three cross-sections $\sigma_a$, $\sigma_e$ and their sum $\sigma_t$. Consider a beam of particles, defined in some way, incident on a block of absorber; for example, the beam may be defined by three scintillation counters in line as in Fig. 26. Suppose that a fourth detector (4) is placed behind the absorber and that its size is large compared to the absorber. When one of the incident particles strikes the block it may either be absorbed, or elastically scattered, or it may emerge without making a collision of any kind. Those particles that undergo diffraction will be scattered into the forward direction with an angular distribution given by equation (6.20). Thus if the detector (4) is placed close to the target, the diffracted particles will pass through it, but it will not record the particles that are absorbed, for they are removed from the beam. Thus the attenuation gives a direct measure of the absorption cross-section; this is known as a 'bad geometry' experiment. On the other hand if (4) is far from the target, most of the diffracted particles will miss it and the attenuation of the beam is then a measure of the total cross-section. This is a 'good geometry' experiment.

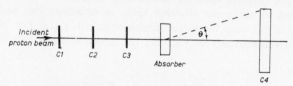

*Fig. 26. A schematic diagram of a scintillation counter telescope*

In practice $\sigma_t$ is obtained by extrapolating the attenuation measured at small angles to zero included solid angle, while $\sigma_a$ is obtained from a similar extrapolation from the large angle data. If Fig. 26 represents a typical arrangement, the number of coincidences $Q$ between all four counters gives a measure of the number of particles which pass through $C4$, while the number of coincidences $T$ between the three defining counters gives a measure of the incident beam intensity. Thus the attenuation $= Q/T = \exp(-x/\lambda)$ where $x$ is the target thickness. Now $\sigma = 1/N\lambda$ so that

$$Q/T = \exp(-xN\sigma) \qquad (6.25)$$

where $N$ is the number of scattering centres per cm³ and $\lambda$ is the mean free path. The elastic scattering cross-section is given by the difference $\sigma_t - \sigma_a$.

Historically, measurements of $\sigma_t$ and $\sigma_a$ were first made using neutrons. Neutrons have the advantage that there are no Coulomb effects to be allowed for and they do not suffer ionization loss. On the other hand most neutron beams have a fairly large energy spread and they cannot be focused or deviated in any way. Further, most neutron detectors are rather inefficient (~0·1 %) and are usually direction-sensitive. By comparison, proton beams can be made monoenergetic, can be focused, and proton detectors usually have a very high efficiency. The main disadvantages in proton experiments are the corrections that must be made for Coulomb scattering and for ionization loss in the targets and detectors.

A typical neutron experiment at a high energy is that of Coor *et al.* (1955) at Brookhaven, who used neutrons of 1400 ± 200 MeV mean energy. The incident neutron beam, at 1° to the primary proton beam, was collimated by a 1″- or 2″-diameter hole in the lead and concrete shielding surrounding the Cosmotron, and then allowed to strike the absorber being investigated. The neutron detector following the target (corresponding to *C*4 in Fig. 26) is shown schematically in Fig. 27. The anticoincidence counter *A*

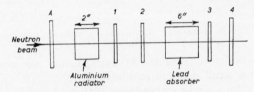

Fig. 27. *A schematic drawing of a scintillation counter telescope for recording neutrons by means of the knock on protons that they produce in an aluminium radiator*

(From COOR *et al. Phys. Rev.* **98**, 1369 (1955))

ensured that no direct protons from the Cosmotron were counted, while counters 1 to 4, which were all plastic scintillators, recorded the knock-on protons produced in the aluminium radiator. The lead absorber between counters 2 and 3 stopped protons of energy less than 400 MeV, so that this figure was the threshold detection energy for the incident neutrons. The attenuation of the beam in passing through an absorber was given by the ratio of neutron counts with and without an absorber in position. A typical proton experiment is that of Booth *et al.* (1957). The arrangement used was essentially that of Fig. 26, where all the counters were plastic scintillators. The proton beam had a mean energy of 895 MeV and was about 1″ in diameter. Counter 4 was 4″ in diameter, and measurements were made for a number of elements, for subtended angles of the detector at the target, of up to 17°.

To obtain $\sigma_e$, other than by the difference $\sigma_t - \sigma_a$, it is necessary to measure the angular distribution of the diffracted nucleons and then to integrate this over all angles. Many determinations of the angular distribution have been made, usually to obtain information on polarization phenomena. Unfortunately the difficulty of making good measurements at small angles, especially for protons, makes it hard to obtain an accurate value for $\sigma_e$. Further, it is also difficult to make measurements at large angles, outside the first diffraction minimum, because of the low intensity of the scattered beam at these angles. In any case, the most significant quantity to determine is $f(0)$, the zero angle scattering amplitude.

## Experimental results and their analysis

A large number of determinations have been made of $\sigma_a$ and $\sigma_t$ by means of 'bad' and 'good' geometry experiments for different elements, at energies up to 900 MeV for protons and 1400 MeV for neutrons. The variation in $\sigma_a$ and $\sigma_t$ with energy for carbon, copper and lead is shown in Fig. 28, which is taken from Chen *et al.* (1955). To within the experimental errors the results obtained for neutrons and protons are the same and thus no distinction between them is made on the figure. The absorption cross-section appears to be sensibly constant over a wide energy range, while the total cross-section appears to pass through a minimum value around 300 MeV. Since $\sigma_t = \sigma_a + \sigma_e$ this suggests that $\sigma_e$ varies in the same way as $\sigma_t$.

All experiments agree that the elastic scattering has the characteristic angular distribution (6.20), at least up to the first minimum, and in principle the half-width at half height of the distribution will yield information about the 'nuclear radius'. Unfortunately this has a clear meaning only in the case of a uniform density model of the nucleus. Fig. 29 shows the results obtained by Ashmore *et al.* (1958) for 350 MeV neutrons scattered from carbon; the full line is the calculated diffraction pattern for a black disc.

The early determinations of the cross-sections at energies above 100 MeV were usually analysed in terms of the simple optical model, using the parameters $k_1$, $K$ and $R$ and the assumption of a complex square well potential. It was shown that the values of $K$ determined from the free nucleon–nucleon cross-sections agreed with those deduced from the measured absorption cross-sections; that $k_1$, although not well determined, gave rise to sensible values of the

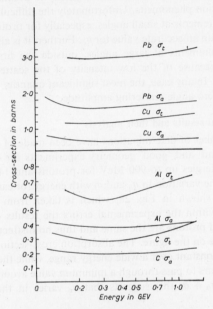

*Fig. 28. Total and absorption cross-sections for C, Al, Cu and Pb as a function of incident nucleon kinetic energy*

(From CHEN *et al. Phys. Rev.* **99**, 857 (1955))

potential $V$; and that reasonable values of $R$ were obtained, although there were discrepancies between the results of different workers and for any given element $R$ appeared to vary with energy. However, with better and more accurate experiments and more detailed analyses, it has become clear that the simple model is unrealistic and cannot fully explain the data. The model at present visualized usually assumes:

(1) that the scattering potential is of the form

$$V(r) = V_c(r) + \boldsymbol{\sigma}.\mathbf{L}\ V_s(r) \tag{6.11}$$

(2) that the nucleon (or potential) distribution is the same as the charge distribution (possibly corrected slightly for the finite range of nucleon–nucleon forces), which is of a form suggested by the electron scattering experiments.

It is then possible to calculate $\sigma_t$ and $\sigma_a$, using equations (6.21) and (6.15) and to compare them with experiment. Some simplifications

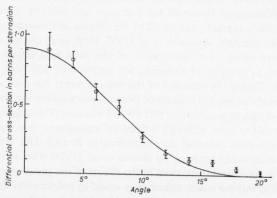

*Fig. 29. The differential cross-section for 350 MeV protons scattered from carbon*
(From ASHMORE et al. Proc. Phys. Soc. A71, 552 (1958))

may be made in these expressions, for the experimental data suggests that, at energies of the order of a few hundred MeV, the real part of the central potential may be small. It can be shown (e.g. Brown, 1957) that the assumption of a purely imaginary central potential means that the spin-orbit potential must be mainly real, otherwise the marked polarization effects found cannot be explained. In fact, if both $V_c$ and $V_s$ are taken to be wholly imaginary the model predicts no polarization effects at all.

With the assumption that $V_c$ is wholly imaginary and $V_s$ wholly real, equations (6.21) and (6.15) reduce to

$$\sigma_t = 4\pi \int_0^\infty \{1 - \exp(-Im\chi_1)\cos\chi_2\}b\,db \qquad (6.26)$$

$$\sigma_a = 2\pi \int_0^\infty \{1 - \exp(-2Im\chi_1)\}b\,db \qquad (6.16)$$

The elastic scattering of nucleons from complex nuclei has mostly been observed by counter techniques, using proton and neutron beams from the large synchro-cyclotrons. Many experiments have been carried out using protons, particularly to observe the polarization phenomena. However, the execution and analysis of neutron experiments is greatly simplified by the absence of Coulomb scattering. For example, Ashmore et al. (1957, 1958) have carried out an extensive series of measurements of the total and elastic cross-sections of a series of elements, for neutrons of 350 MeV mean energy. Within the accuracy of the measurements the data yielded the result that $Im f(0)$ (calculated from $\sigma_t$) was equal to the observed value of $f(0)$, thus indicating that $Re f(0)$ was zero. This suggests that $V$ is small or zero, although it must be remembered that the complex spin-orbit potential may contribute to $Re f(0)$. This work has been extensively analysed by Brown et al. (1958) who show that there is considerable freedom in the choice of the parameters to fit the observations unless reference is made to polarization data. In fact, these authors used a value for the strength of the spin-orbit potential derived from the available polarization measurements.

At a higher energy Booth et al. (1958) have measured the absorption and total cross-sections for a number of elements for neutrons of 765 MeV mean energy. These authors showed that if it was assumed that $V = 0$ and that $V_s$ was completely real, with $W$ determined directly by the individual nucleon–nucleon cross-sections, then the calculated values of $\sigma_a$ agreed well with their results. Further, the corresponding calculations for protons of 860 and 895 MeV and neutrons of 1400 MeV, gave good agreement with the experimental data available at these energies. The values of $W$ used were of the order of 50–60 MeV.

## Polarization phenomena

An unpolarized beam of particles which have intrinsic spin may be defined as a beam in which the spin vectors of the individual particles are orientated at random. If spin-selective nuclear forces exist, the scattering by a target of an unpolarized beam of particles will yield a partially polarized beam, that is, one which contains particles with preferred spin directions. At low energies forces are known to exist which couple the spin, $\sigma$, of the incident nucleon with its orbital angular momentum, $L$, about the scattering centre, and are called spin-orbit forces. It is found experimentally that similar forces exist at high energies ($E > 50$ MeV), and it is possible therefore to produce polarized proton beams. In terms of the optical model of the nucleus, the presence of a spin-orbit force can be represented by a spin-orbit potential, $V_s$, which is added to the central potential, $V_c$.

The effect of a spin-orbit scattering potential may be understood by considering the following classical picture, which follows, to some extent, the treatment given by Fermi (1955). Let the central potential be represented by a square well, and let this potential be purely imaginary, representing the fact that the nucleus absorbs the incident wave. This potential will give rise to a scattered amplitude of the form $\dfrac{J_1 (kR \sin \theta)}{\sin \theta}$ which falls to zero at $\theta \sim 1.22\lambda/2R$.

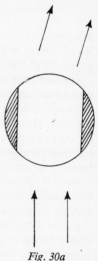

The presence of a spin-orbit force means that an incident particle can recognize whether it is on the right or the left of the centre of the target nucleus; the short range of nuclear forces therefore implies that the effect of the spin-orbit force is confined to the surface layer of the nucleus. The shaded region of Fig. 30a indicates the region of the nucleus in which one could expect the incident particle to feel the effect of the spin-orbit force. Let this force be represented by a spin-orbit potential as in (6.11). For, say, a proton of spin up, this potential will have opposite sign on opposite sides of the nucleus, and will have the form

*Fig. 30a*

shown in Fig. 30b. Fig. 30c shows the form of the purely imaginary central potential.

The amplitude of the wave scattered from the spin-orbit potential will be zero in the forward direction, for the contributions from the two sides of the nucleus will interfere destructively. At angles other than zero, the contributions gradually come into phase, and there will be a series of maxima and minima at angles given by $2R \sin \theta = (2n + 1)\lambda/2$ and $2R \sin \theta = n\lambda$ respectively, corresponding to Young's fringes in classical wave optics. The phase of the resultant scattered amplitude, from the two sides of the spin-orbit potential,

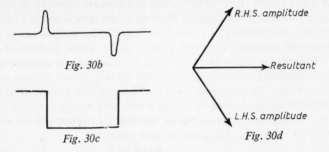

Fig. 30b

Fig. 30c

R.H.S. amplitude

Resultant

L.H.S. amplitude

Fig. 30d

will always be half-way between the phase of the contributions (Fig. 30d). Thus it will be either in phase, or out of phase, with the amplitude of the wave scattered by the central potential.

The scattering amplitudes as a function of angle, resulting from the central potential alone, and from the spin-orbit potential alone, as seen by spin-up protons, and by spin-down protons, are shown in Fig. 30e. The differential cross-sections are shown in Fig. 30f for the central potential only, in which case the angular distribution is the same for protons with spin up and spin down, and for the combination of central and spin-orbit potential, curves being given separately for spin-up and spin-down protons. It can be seen from this diagram that, at any given angle, there are more particles of spin up than spin down on one side, and the converse is true for the other side. Thus a polarized beam is obtained at practically any angle, but the magnitude of the polarization varies with angle; the beam is 100% polarized at points X and Y in the figure, which are near to the diffraction minima. This is always true, as the strength of the spin-orbit potential is small ($\sim 1$ MeV) compared with that of the central potential ($\sim 50$ MeV).

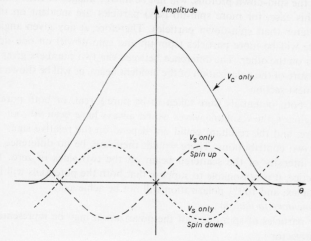

*Fig. 30e*

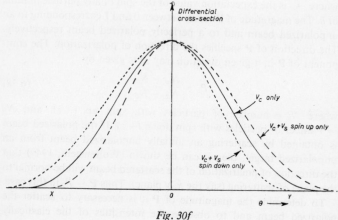

*Fig. 30f*

Consider now a polarized beam striking a second scatterer. The same argument as that given above may be used, but the corresponding curves for the differential cross-sections for the spin-up protons, and the spin-down protons, will not be mirror images of each other in this case, for more spin-up (say) particles are incident on the scatterer than spin-down particles. Therefore, at any given angle, there will be more particles (spin up and spin down) on one side than on the other. The difference between the two numbers gives a measure of the polarization of the incident beam, as will be shown in the next section.

If both potentials were taken to be purely real, or both purely imaginary, the resultant waves would always have been 90° out of phase, and the resultant could not depend on the relative signs of the two contributions. There would, therefore, be no difference in the intensity of the scattered beam on the two sides of zero. In practice, it is reasonable to suppose that both the potentials will be complex, and 100% polarization will not be achieved.

*Elementary formalism*

For particles of spin one half the polarization may be represented by a vector

$$\mathbf{P} = 2\langle \mathbf{s} \rangle \tag{6.27}$$

where $\langle \mathbf{s} \rangle$ is the expectation value of the spin of any particle in units of $\hbar$. The magnitude of $\mathbf{P}$ varies between 0 and 1 corresponding to an unpolarized beam and to a perfectly polarized beam respectively. The direction of $\mathbf{P}$ specifies the direction of polarization. The component of $\mathbf{P}$ in a given direction (say $z$) is given by

$$P_z = \frac{N_\alpha - N_\beta}{N_\alpha + N_\beta} \tag{6.28}$$

where $N_\alpha$ = number of particles with spin up ($+z$), and $N_\beta$ = number of particles with spin down ($-z$). If the polarized beam is obtained by scattering an initially unpolarized beam from an unpolarized target, then it can be shown (Wolfenstein, 1949) that the direction of polarization of the scattered beam will be normal to the plane of scattering (say the $x$, $y$ plane). Thus $\mathbf{P} = P_z$ in this case.

To determine the magnitude of $\mathbf{P}$ it is necessary to scatter the polarized beam and to observe the intensities of the elastically scattered particles left and right, in the plane of the first scattering. This is a double scattering experiment. If the asymmetry, $\varepsilon$, is defined as

$$\varepsilon = \frac{R - L}{R + L} \qquad (6.29)$$

where $R$ and $L$ are the number of particles scattered to the right and left respectively, then

$$\varepsilon = P_1(\theta_1)P_2(\theta_2) \qquad (6.30)$$

where $P_1$ is the magnitude of the polarization produced at an angle $\theta_1$ at the first target and $P_2$ that produced at $\theta_2$ at the second target. If $\theta_1 = \theta_2$, and the two targets are made of the same material, then

$$P_1(\theta_1) = P_2(\theta_2) = P(\theta) = \pm\sqrt{\varepsilon} \qquad (6.31)$$

A separate experiment must be performed to determine the sign of the polarization. The importance of distinguishing between elastically and inelastically scattered particles will be discussed later.

Expression (6.30) may be derived using the following argument. Let $N_\alpha{}^R(1) + N_\beta{}^R(1)$ denote the number of particles scattered from the first target (1) at an angle $\theta_1$ to the right (superscript $R$); the subscripts $\alpha$ and $\beta$ refer to particles with spin up ($+z$) and spin down ($-z$) respectively. This number will be proportional to the differential scattering cross-section $\sigma_1(\theta_1)$ at that angle, that is

$$N_\alpha{}^R(1) + N_\beta{}^R(1) \propto \sigma_1(\theta_1)$$

and also
$$P_1(\theta_1) = (N_\alpha{}^R(1) - N_\beta{}^R(1))/(N_\alpha{}^R(1) + N_\beta{}^R(1))$$
Therefore
$$N_\alpha{}^R(1) \propto \sigma_1(\theta_1)[1 + P_1(\theta_1)]$$
and
$$N_\beta{}^R(1) \propto \sigma_1(\theta_1)[1 - P_1(\theta_1)]$$

This particular beam is then allowed to strike a second target, denoted by (2). If $\alpha$, $\beta$ and $R$ have the same meaning as above, and if $L$ denotes a scatter to the left, then the number of particles scattered to the right, with spin up and spin down respectively, is given by

$$N_\alpha{}^R(2) \propto \sigma_1(\theta_1)\sigma_2(\theta_2)[1 + P_1(\theta_1)][1 + P_2(\theta_2)]$$
and
$$N_\beta{}^R(2) \propto \sigma_1(\theta_1)\sigma_2(\theta_2)[1 - P_1(\theta_1)][1 - P_2(\theta_2)]$$

Similarly for the scatters to the left at angle $\theta_2$

$$N_\alpha{}^L(2) \propto \sigma_1(\theta_1)\sigma_2(\theta_2)[1 + P_1(\theta_1)][1 - P_2(\theta_2)]$$
and
$$N_\beta{}^L(2) \propto \sigma_1(\theta_1)\sigma_2(\theta_2)[1 - P_1(\theta_1)][1 + P_2(\theta_2)]$$

K

In these equations $\sigma_2(\theta_2)$ is the differential cross-section for scattering at angle $(\theta_2)$ from the second target.

The total number scattered to the right from the second target, $R$, at angle $\theta_2$, is therefore

$$R = N_\alpha{}^R(2) + N_\beta{}^R(2) \propto \sigma_1(\theta_1)\sigma_2(\theta_2)[1 + P_1(\theta_1)P_2(\theta_2)]$$

and to the left

$$L = N_\alpha{}^L(2) + N_\beta{}^L(2) \propto \sigma_1(\theta_1)\sigma_2(\theta_2)[1 - P_1(\theta_1)P_2(\theta_2)]$$

Then $\quad \varepsilon = (R - L)/(R + L) = P_1(\theta_1)P_2(\theta_2) \qquad (6.30)$

and if $\theta_1 = \theta_2$, and if the materials of the two targets are the same, then the measured asymmetry gives the magnitude of the polarization of the beam from the first target at angle $\theta = \theta_1 = \theta_2$, for the material in question. The variation of polarization with angle for the same material, or any other material, can then be investigated by keeping the first scattering material, and angle, constant, i.e. fixing $P_1(\theta_1)$, and varying the conditions at the second target. A measurement of the asymmetry, at angle $\theta_2$, then gives $P_2(\theta_2)$ directly from (6.30). Note that the preceding discussion assumes that the spin of the target nucleus is zero, for both first and second scatterings.

*Triple scattering experiments*

A double scattering experiment simply measures the polarization of the beam produced by the first scattering process, that is, the component of the polarization vector **P**, perpendicular to the scattering plane. A triple scattering experiment enables the change (if any), produced by the scattering at the second target, to be investigated. There are several variations of triple scattering experiment, which depend upon the plane in which observations are carried out. For example, consider the case when all three scatterings occur in the same plane. The number of particles scattered from the second target at an angle $\theta_2$ to the right is given by

$$N_\alpha{}^R(2) \propto \sigma_1(\theta_1)\sigma_2(\theta_2)[1 + P_1(\theta_1)][1 + P_2(\theta_2)]$$

and $\qquad N_\beta{}^R(2) \propto \sigma_1(\theta_1)\sigma_2(\theta_2)[1 - P_1(\theta_1)][1 - P_2(\theta_2)]$

Therefore the polarization, $p'$, of this particular beam is

$$p' = \frac{N_\alpha{}^R - N_\beta{}^R}{N_\alpha{}^R + N_\beta{}^R} = \frac{P_1(\theta_1) + P_2(\theta_2)}{1 + P_1(\theta_1)P_2(\theta_2)}$$

Now this expression is true provided that there is no spin-flip scattering, that is, no change in spin direction by any particle. If there is spin-flip scattering then

$$p' = \frac{P_1 + DP_2}{1 + P_1 P_2} \quad (\text{suppose } \theta_1 = \theta_2)$$

and $D$ is the *depolarization coefficient* which measures the probability that the incoming particles, to the second target, maintain their spin direction. If the beam $p'$ is now allowed to strike a third target the measured asymmetry, $\varepsilon_3$, at an angle $\theta_3$, will be

$$\varepsilon_3 = p' P_3(\theta_3)$$

Since $P_1$, $P_2$ and $P_3$ can all be determined, a measurement of $\varepsilon_3$ gives $p'$ and thus $D$ directly. If the three scatterings occur in planes that are successively perpendicular, then a rotation parameter $R$ may be defined. If a magnetic field is inserted between the first and second scatterings, the average spin vector precesses about the field direction with an angular frequency which is larger than that of the frequency of rotation of the momentum vector, which states the direction of motion of the proton, due to the anomalous magnetic moment of the proton. Thus a longitudinal component of polarization is introduced, which is associated with a further parameter $A$. In nucleon–nucleon scattering measurement of parameters such as $D$, $R$ and $A$ gives additional relations between the different phase shifts (Chapter VII, p. 151). In the case of nucleon–nucleus scattering it is found experimentally that $D = 1$ for a large number of nuclei; that is, they behave, from the point of view of elastic scattering, as spin-zero nuclei. The rotation parameter $R$ is of more value in that it is possible to predict it, using the optical model. Reasonable agreement with experiment has been obtained.

*Experiments*

The first experiment to demonstrate large polarization effects at high energies was carried out by Oxley *et al.* (1954) using 225 MeV protons from the Rochester synchrocyclotron. The protons were scattered at 19° from a carbon (or polythene) target within the machine. The second scattering was at 27°, again from a carbon (or polythene) target; the energy of the scattered protons was about

200 MeV. If $P$ (19°) and $P$ (27°) were assumed to be the same, the results obtained gave a value for the mean polarization, produced by scattering from carbon, of $43 \pm 8\%$, and from hydrogen of $22 + 4\%$.

Many laboratories have since carried out extensive studies of polarization phenomena associated with both complex nuclei and with hydrogen. The most extensive work is that of Chamberlain *et al.* (1956) at Berkeley, who used protons of 315 MeV. The experimental arrangement used by these authors is sketched in Fig. 31.

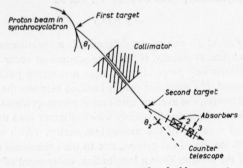

Fig. 31. Schematic diagram of a double scattering
experiment

The target in the synchrocyclotron was beryllium and the beam of protons scattered out at 13° was found to be 76% polarized. This beam was used for all the subsequent experiments. Elements ranging from Be to Ta were used as second targets and the angular region investigated was from $1\frac{1}{2}°$ to approximately 25° laboratory angle. The particles scattered by the second target were detected by a triple counter telescope; different thicknesses of absorber could be placed between the first and second scintillation counters in order to vary the threshold detection energy of the apparatus.

The important results of these, and other experiments, up to 660 MeV may be summarized as:

(1) The curves of polarization as a function of angle show maxima
and minima, which are very pronounced if the scattering is

purely elastic (see below and Fig. 32). The minima lie close to the positions of the diffraction minima.

(2) Elements of similar atomic weight produce similar polarizations.

(3) The value of the polarization rises from almost zero at 50 MeV to a maximum value of nearly 100% at about 200 MeV; it then decreases slowly to around 50% at 400 MeV and remains at this value to 660 MeV. These figures are for carbon. It should be borne in mind that most experiments have not resolved the elastic and inelastically scattered protons from each other, so that the values quoted for the polarization are only lower limits.

(4) With increase of the atomic weight of the scattering material at a fixed energy the magnitude of the first maximum of the polarization (as a function of angle) appears to decrease.

It has become clear since early 1956 that to compare the data with any theoretical predictions it is necessary to distinguish between elastically and inelastically scattered particles. An inelastically scattered particle may transfer energy to the struck nucleus and raise it to an excited state. If this happens it is customary to talk of 'scattering from an excited level'. In the case of carbon the three lowest energy levels of the $C^{12}$ nucleus are at 4·43, 7·65 and 9·61 MeV. It is clearly rather difficult to distinguish between high-energy protons which have been elastically scattered and those which have lost 4·4 MeV to a carbon nucleus. Nevertheless this has been accomplished in recent experiments by using proton beams with a very small energy spread and by measuring the energies of the scattered protons with a range telescope consisting of several scintillation counters interspersed with the absorbers (see Chesnut *et al.*, 1956; Hafner, 1958). Two important results have been obtained:

(1) near the diffraction minimum there may be two or three times as many particles scattered from the 4·43 MeV level as are elastically scattered.

(2) also near to the diffraction minimum the polarization of the inelastically scattered protons may be large and positive while that of the pure elastically scattered particles may even be negative. This

feature of the data is illustrated in Fig. 32 which shows the results of
Alphonce *et al.* (1957) for 155 MeV protons scattered from carbon.

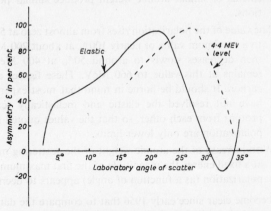

*Fig. 32. The asymmetry after the second scattering of 155
MeV protons (a) elastically scattered from Carbon (full
line) and (b) inelastically scattered from the 4·4 MeV
excited state of Carbon (dotted line)*

(From ALPHONCE *et al. Nuclear Physics*, **4**, 672 (1957))

*The sign of the polarization*

The determination of the sign of the polarization makes use of the
facts (*a*) that depolarization does not occur when fast polarized
protons are slowed down (this has been shown both theoretically
and experimentally) and (*b*) that the scattering of 1–10 MeV protons
by helium has been extensively studied so that an analysis of the
data yields a *unique* set of phase-shifts. From the phase-shifts it is
possible to calculate the left and right differential cross-sections for
proton–He scattering, and thus the left–right asymmetry, for the two
different possible choices of the sign of the polarization of the incident proton beam. The original experiment was carried out by
Brinkworth and Rose (1956) who slowed down 135 MeV protons,
elastically scattered from carbon, to between 0–10 MeV and then
allowed them to pass into helium gas. The scattered protons were
recorded in nuclear emulsions. The initial scatter was to the left.

The sign of the polarization vector is defined by $\mathbf{P} = P(\theta)\mathbf{n}$ where $\mathbf{n} = \mathbf{k} \times \mathbf{k}'$ and where $\mathbf{k}$ and $\mathbf{k}'$ are the wave numbers (momenta for $\hbar = 1$) of the incident and scattered particles respectively. Thus for a left-hand scatter in the $x$, $y$ plane the product $\mathbf{k} \times \mathbf{k}'$ is a vector which points upwards $(+z)$. The results of the experiment were consistent with the polarization vector being directed upwards. This sign of the polarization is obtained if one chooses the sign of $V_s$ to be the same as that used in the shell model.

It is of interest to note that the sign of $V_s$ is also given by an analysis of the small-angle polarization data at the high energies. At the small angles it is necessary to include in the expression for the polarization a term which allows for the interaction of the magnetic moment of the incident proton with the Coulomb field of the target nucleus. This term is spin-dependent, and therefore the predicted value of $\mathbf{P}$ at any given angle will depend on the sign taken for the polarization vector. Heckrotte (1956) has analysed some small-angle $p$–C polarization data at 316 MeV and has shown that the data are definitely in favour of the sign of $V_s$ to be the same as that used in the shell model.

*Analysis of polarization data*

Most analyses of polarization phenomena have employed the optical model of the nucleus, which has been extensively discussed earlier in this chapter. The scattering potential is assumed to be of the form (6.11) where, by analogy with spin-orbit potentials which recur in a number of other physical situations, the functional form of $V_s$ is taken to be

$$V_s(r) = -\gamma \frac{\hbar}{2M^2c^2} \cdot \frac{1}{r}\frac{d}{dr}V_c(r) \qquad (6.32)$$

where $\gamma$ is a numerical constant. It has been shown (e.g. Fernbach *et al.*, 1955) that at least above 100 MeV a radial dependence of $V_s$ of this form is a simple consequence of the nucleon–nucleon interaction. To account for the magnitude of the observed polarization effects $\gamma$ turns out to be about 15, which is approximately the same value as is required for the low-energy shell model of the nucleus. It is clear from (6.32) that $V_s(r)$ and $V_c(r)$ cannot be treated as two independent parameters; once $V_c(r)$ is known the only remaining parameter is the strength of the spin-orbit potential, $C$, expressed by the term $C = \gamma\hbar/2M^2c^2$.

It has been shown by Heckrotte (1956) that the small-angle polarization results for 316 MeV protons scattered from carbon cannot be explained unless $V_s$ is assumed to have an imaginary part. This may be allowed for in (6.32) by allowing the numerical constant $\gamma$ to have real and imaginary parts. Most theoretical papers, however, have assumed $V_s$ to be wholly real. It has already been mentioned that if $V_c$ is also taken to be wholly real then it can be shown that no polarization effects would be observed. Similarly, there is no polarization if $V_c$ and $V_s$ are both taken to be completely imaginary. A polarization of 100 % is obtained from $V_c$ completely imaginary and $V_s$ completely real. The ordinary scattering data indicates that $V_c$ is largely imaginary at high energies, so that it is reasonable to expect appreciable polarization effects.

Detailed calculations of polarization as a function of scattering angle, based on the optical model, have been made by several authors (e.g. Sternheimer, 1954, 1955; Fernbach *et al.*, 1955). By a suitable choice of parameters it has been possible to obtain a fairly reasonable fit to most of the data at angles less than that corresponding to the first diffraction minimum. The sparse experimental data that exist for *elastically* scattered particles appear to give a good fit to the predictions of the theoretical models.

The energy dependence of the polarization is connected with the energy dependence of (*a*) the real and imaginary parts of $V_c$, and (*b*) the strength of spin-orbit potential, represented by $\gamma$ (or $C$). Sternheimer (1955), for example, has shown quantitatively that the decrease in polarization below 130 MeV may be explained by a decrease in the imaginary part of $V_c$. Above 130 MeV several experiments suggest that $V_c$ is almost completely imaginary; the decrease of polarization with increasing energy may then be due to a decrease of the strength of the spin-orbit potential, or to a change in the relative magnitudes of the real and imaginary parts of the spin-orbit potential.

The observation that the first polarization maximum (as a function of angle) decreases in magnitude with increase of atomic number may be attributed to Coulomb effects. Normal Coulomb scattering is not spin-dependent and cannot give rise to polarization effects; the addition of Coulomb scattering to the nuclear scattering, which does give rise to polarization, will therefore lower the magnitude of the polarization that is observed. The maximum angle at which this effect is appreciable increases with increase of the atomic number of the scattering material.

## Summary

At the present time it is clear that the experimental data are insufficient to determine completely the various parameters of an optical model of the nucleus which assumes complex central, and spin-orbit, potentials. Very approximately one may say that the real part of the central potential decreases from about 50 MeV at zero bombarding energy to about 20 MeV at 100 MeV; above this energy it probably becomes less as the energy rises and may be very small or zero above 300 MeV. The imaginary part of the central potential is of the order of 10–20 MeV up to around 300 MeV and then appears to rise to $\sim 60$ MeV at around 800 MeV. The spin-orbit potential is of the order of 1–2 MeV; its variation with energy is not known, while little can be said about the relative magnitudes of the real and imaginary parts of the potential.

It has been shown by several authors (e.g. Riesenfeld and Watson, 1956; Bethe, 1958) that a close connexion exists between nucleon–nucleon scattering and nucleon–nucleus scattering. Bethe has shown that the correct magnitudes of the potentials $V_c$ and $V_s$ used in the optical model analysis, can in fact be derived from the nucleon–nucleon phase shifts. One may argue in the reverse direction in order to try to decide between the various sets of phase shifts that exist at present. Unfortunately the data available are not sufficiently accurate or detailed to allow any phase-shift solutions to be rejected.

## BIBLIOGRAPHY

BETHE, H. A. and MORRISON, P. 1957. *Elementary Nuclear Theory*, 2nd Ed. John Wiley. Ch. 17 (polarization). Ch. 20 (nuclear reactions – mostly low energy).

FERMI, E. 1955. *Nuovo Cimento*, **II**, Supplemento No. 1, 84 (polarization).

FESHBACH, H. 1958. *Ann. Rev. Nuc. Sci.* **8**, 49 (optical model).

LANE, A. M. 1957. *Rev. Mod. Phys.* **29**, 191 (nuclear reactions).

TAYLOR, A. E. 1957. *Reports on Progress in Physics*, **20**, 86 (nuclear reactions and polarization).

WATTENBERG, A. 1957. *Handbuch der Physik*, **40**, 450, Springer (nuclear reactions).

WEISSKOPF, V. F. 1957. *Rev. Mod. Phys.* **29**, 174 (nuclear reactions).

WOLFENSTEIN, L. 1956. *Ann. Rev. Nuc. Sci.* **6**, 43 (polarization).

# REFERENCES

ALPHONCE, R., JOHANSSON, A. and TIBELL, G. 1957. *Nuclear Physics*, **3**, 185.

ASHMORE, A., JARVIS, R. G., MATHER, D. S. and SEN, S. K. 1957. *Proc. Phys. Soc.* **A70**, 745.

ASHMORE, A., MATHER, D. S. and SEN, S. K. 1958. *Proc. Phys. Soc.* **71**, 552.

BETHE, H. A. 1958. *Annals of Physics*, **3**, 190.

BETHE, H. A. and WILSON, R. R. 1951. *Phys. Rev.* **83**, 690.

BOOTH, N. E., LEDLEY, B., WALKER, D. and WHITE, D. H. 1957. *Proc. Phys. Soc.* **A70**, 209.

BOOTH, N. E., LEDLEY, B. and HUTCHINSON, G. W. 1958. *Proc. Phys. Soc.* **71**, 293.

BRINKWORTH, M. J. and ROSE, B. 1956. *Nuovo Cimento*, **III**, 195.

BROWN, G. E. 1957. *Proc. Phys. Soc.* **A70**, 361.

BROWN, G. E., ASHMORE, A. and NORDHAGEN, R. 1958. *Proc. Phys. Soc.* **71**, 565.

CAMERINI, U., LOCK, W. O. and PERKINS, D. H. 1952. *Progress in Cosmic Ray Physics*, **I**, 1. North-Holland, Amsterdam.

CHAMBERLAIN, O., SEGRÈ, E., TRIPP, R. D., WIEGAND, C. and YPSILANTIS, T. 1956. *Phys. Rev.* **102**, 1659.

CHEN, F. F., LEAVITT, C. P. and SHAPIRO, A. M. 1955. *Phys. Rev.* **99**, 857.

CHESNUT, W. G., HAFNER, E. M. and ROBERTS, A. 1956. *Phys. Rev.* **104**, 449.

COOR, T., HILL, D. A., HORNYAK, W. F., SMITH, L. W. and SNOW, G. A. 1955. *Phys. Rev.* **98**, 1369.

FERNBACH, S., HECKROTTE, W. and LEPORE, J. V. 1955. *Phys. Rev.* **97**, 1059.

FERNBACH, S., SERBER, R. and TAYLOR, T. B. 1949. *Phys. Rev.* **75**, 1352.

HAFNER, E. M. 1958. *Phys. Rev.* **111**, 297.

HECKROTTE, W. 1956. *Phys. Rev.* **101**, 1406.

HOFSTADTER, R. 1956. *Rev. Mod. Phys.* **28**, 214.

MALENKA, B. J. 1954. *Phys. Rev.* **95**, 522.

OXLEY, C. L., CARTWRIGHT, W. F. and ROUVINA, J. 1954. *Phys. Rev.* **93**, 806.

RIESENFELD, W. B. and WATSON, K. M. 1956. *Phys. Rev.* **102**, 1157.

SERBER, R. 1947. *Phys. Rev.* **72**, 1008.

STERNHEIMER, R. M. 1954. *Phys. Rev.* **95**, 587; 1955. ibid. **100**, 886.

WOLFENSTEIN, L. 1949. *Phys. Rev.* **75**, 1664.

# CHAPTER VII

# Nucleon–Nucleon Elastic Scattering

The scattering of nucleons by nucleons is more fundamental than nucleon-nucleus scattering, but again the interpretation of the data is complicated by the presence of the virtual meson link between the nucleons. Until a satisfactory theory of meson–nucleon scattering has been evolved it is hardly to be expected that the theory of nucleon-nucleon collisions will be very specific. In fact the major theoretical efforts at energies above 100 MeV have been directed towards attempts to find a unique set of phase-shifts which will describe the scattering, and to construct potentials which will yield the observed phase-shifts. These attempts have not met with complete success, although considerable advances have been made in recent years.

The experimental methods used to determine the various cross-sections are similar, and in some cases identical, with those described in the previous chapter. The total cross-sections are usually determined from 'good geometry' experiments, while the absorption cross-sections are deduced from an extrapolation of the 'bad geometry' measurements. In nucleon–nucleon scattering true absorption does not occur; the equivalent process is that of meson production, and in this context is known as *inelastic* scattering. (Meson production is but one absorption process that may occur in nucleon-nucleus scattering.) A collision in which the incident nucleon shares its energy with the struck nucleon, and in which no mesons are produced, is known as an *elastic* scattering. It is important to bear in mind that these terms are used in different senses in different contexts.

In this chapter we shall discuss the measurement of the elastic, inelastic and total cross-sections, and then concentrate on the behaviour and interpretation of the elastic scattering data. The different inelastic processes which lead to pion production are discussed in detail in the next chapter.

## Neutron–proton scattering

### Total cross-sections

A typical *n–p* scattering experiment is that of Nedzel (1954) which
will be described in order to illustrate the approach which is usually
adopted. Nedzel used neutrons of $410 \pm 20$ MeV mean energy from
the Chicago synchrocyclotron; his experimental arrangement is
sketched in Fig. 33. The neutrons were obtained by bombarding a
$2'' \times 1''$ beryllium target by 450 MeV protons. After collimation to
a beam $1''$ in diameter the neutrons first struck a thin polythene block,

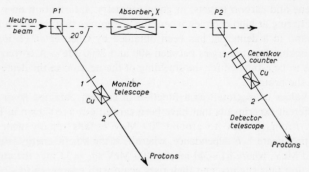

*Fig. 33. Schematic diagram of the counter arrangement used in an
n–p scattering experiment*

(From NEDZEL. *Phys. Rev.* **94**, 174 (1954))

P1, and recoil protons ejected at 20° to the beam direction were
counted by two scintillation counters in coincidence. A copper
absorber was placed between the two counters to stop protons of low
energy, so that those appreciably below 410 MeV would not be
counted. This constituted the monitor telescope which gave a measure
of the intensity of the incident beam. To obtain the *n–p* total cross-
section, attenuation measurements were made, using cyclohexane,
benzene and carbon in the absorber position, X, thus yielding two
independent differences. The intensity of the neutron beam, after
passing through the absorber, X, was measured by counting recoil
protons from a second polythene scatterer, P2, with a counter telescope consisting of two liquid scintillators separated by a Čerenkov

counter and a copper absorber. The Čerenkov counter was a 4"-thick Lucite radiator viewed by a photomultiplier, and it counted only protons of energy greater than 330 MeV ($\beta = 0.67$). Similar experiments have been carried out, using neutrons of energy between 300 and 600 MeV obtained from the Russian 660-MeV synchrocyclotron and these have been summarized in English by Dzhelepov *et al.* (1956a, b). One of these experiments will be described in more detail later. The experiment of Coor *et al.* (1955) at 1400 MeV has been described earlier (p. 120). The $n$–$p$ cross-section was determined by measuring the difference in the attentuation of polythene and carbon targets, in good geometry. Information on $p$–'$n$' scattering at high energies, where the '$n$' signifies that the neutron is bound in a deuteron, has been obtained by Chen *et al.* (1956) at Brookhaven, at energies between 400 and 2600 MeV. A correction has to be estimated for the shielding of the neutron in the deuteron by the proton.

Values of $\sigma_{np}$(total) as a function of energy, obtained from the different experiments that have been carried out, are shown in Fig. 34. From 10 MeV to around 200 MeV $\sigma_t$ falls rapidly with an approximate $1/E$ dependence, where $E$ is the kinetic energy. From 200 MeV, where $\sigma_t = 40$ mb, to 400 MeV ($\sigma_t = 33$ mb) the cross-section falls slightly, and then rises again with energy up to 42 mb at 1400 MeV. The $p$–'$n$' data of Chen *et al.* suggests that at higher energies the cross-section decreases to about 38 mb at 2500 MeV.

*The differential elastic cross-section*

The energy threshold for the production of a pion in a nucleon–nucleon collision is 296 MeV. Below this energy, therefore, the scattering is purely elastic, so that $\sigma$(total) $= \sigma$(elastic), and it is relatively easy to measure the differential elastic scattering cross-section, either by observing the recoil proton or the scattered neutron. Above 296 MeV pion production becomes increasingly important and $\sigma$(total) $= \sigma$(elastic) $+ \sigma$(inelastic).

To identify elastic scattering events it is necessary either to observe both the scattered neutron and the recoil proton, or to measure the energy and angle of one of the particles. For example, at 580 MeV Dzhelepov *et al.* (1956b) used a scintillation counter telescope, containing absorbers, to detect the recoil protons, and to obtain an estimate of their energy. Protons associated with meson producing collisions will have a much lower energy than those of elastically scattered protons and will not be recorded by the counter telescope. In all experiments the absolute values of the differential scattering cross-sections are determined by normalizing the observed angular distribution to the total elastic cross-section. Above 300 MeV this

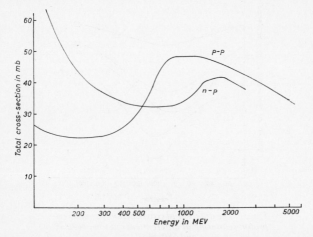

*Fig. 34. The total cross-section for proton–proton and neutron–proton scattering as a function of incident proton energy*

Largely taken from data quoted by CHEN *et al. Phys. Rev.* **103**, 211 (1956) )

cross-section is taken to be the difference between the measured total cross-section and the measured cross-section for pion production.

At low energies ($\sim$100 MeV) the recoil protons have been detected by means of proportional counters, scintillation counters, and in hydrogen-filled diffusion chambers. At higher energies neutron detectors of the type shown in Fig. 27 have been used. Typical experimental results for the differential cross-section are shown in Fig. 35. Below 50 MeV the distribution is almost isotropic, but as the incident neutron energy rises it becomes peaked at both small and large angles. At 90 MeV it is approximately symmetrical about a minimum value at 90°. At 130 MeV the minimum is at 80°, but between 290 and 600 MeV it occurs at about 100°. The asymmetry about the minimum appears to change in nature between 300

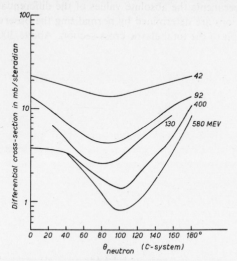

*Fig. 35. The differential cross-section for neutron–proton scattering at different energies between 42 and 580 MeV*

(Largely based on data given by w. n. hess. *Rev. Mod. Phys.* **30**, 368 (1958) )

and 600 MeV. The strong forward peaking is associated with the presence of inelastic scattering (absorption), while the backward peaking is due to charge-exchange scattering. A discussion of the interpretation of the results is given later.

*Separation of the elastic and inelastic n–p cross-sections*

There is relatively little information on the magnitudes of these cross-sections at energies above 400 MeV, other than a knowledge of their sum, that is, the total cross-section. At 580 MeV the Russian work mentioned earlier gives $\sigma$(inelastic) $= 10 \pm 2$ mb and $\sigma$ (total) $= 36 \pm 2$ mb, which yields $\sigma$(elastic) $= 26 \pm 3$ mb; the latter figure is close to the $p$–$p$ elastic scattering cross-section at this energy. At 970 MeV Batson *et al.* (1959), using a diffusion cloud chamber filled with deuterium, estimate the total $p$–'$n$' cross-section to be $38 \pm 3$ mb, and the elastic $p$–'$n$' cross-section to be about $16 \pm 4$ mb. Thus the elastic cross-section appears to decrease rather rapidly with increasing energy, while the inelastic cross-section increases, for the total cross-section rises only slightly with increasing energy.

## Proton–proton scattering

### Total cross-sections

A simple good geometry attenuation experiment, as used in $n$-$p$ work, is not in general possible for protons of energy less than about 100 MeV, for their range in the scatterer used is comparable with, or less than, their mean free path for interaction. This is particularly true if the experiment is carried out using carbon and polythene absorbers in order to obtain the $p$-$p$ scattering data. If a liquid-hydrogen target is used, a direct attenuation experiment can be carried out, but very few such measurements have been made. Below 350 MeV, that is in the region in which the $\sigma$(elastic scattering) is equal to $\sigma$(total), most values of $\sigma_{pp}$ total have been derived from differential measurements, extrapolated to $\theta = 0°$, and integrated. The differential cross-section is essentially isotropic between 100 and 400 MeV and $\sigma_t = 2\pi \times$ average $\sigma(\theta)$. ($2\pi$ because the particles are identical.) A direct attenuation experiment at 135 MeV by Taylor and Wood (1956), using a liquid hydrogen target, has given results in good agreement with those obtained from the differential measurements.

Above 400 MeV an extensive series of good geometry attenuation experiments has been carried out by Chen *et al.* (1956) at Brookhaven. They used an external proton beam which, after passing through 3 scintillation counters, was incident on the absorber being used, which was either carbon or polythene. A fourth counter, $6''$ in diameter, was placed behind the absorber to detect the unscattered particles. Measurements of the difference in attenuation between the carbon and polythene absorbers were made at a series of energies from 410 to 2600 MeV. A liquid hydrogen target was also used at two energies; the results agreed with those derived from the carbon–polythene measurements. A series of $D_2O - H_2O$ difference experiments were also carried out to provide information on the $p$–'$n$'

L

total cross-section. The results of the *p–p* work of Chen *et al.*, together with the lower energy data, are shown in Fig. 34. The total cross-section falls rapidly from 72 mb at 40 MeV, to about 23 mb at 140 MeV, and then remains practically constant at 23 mb up to 350 MeV. Above this energy pion production begins to play an important role and the total cross-section rises to a maximum value of 48 mb at 850 MeV and remains at this value to about 1500 MeV. At higher energies the meagre data suggest that the total cross-section falls slowly with energy.

## Differential cross-section for elastic scattering

The cross-section for elastic *p–p* scattering is relatively easy to determine by virtue of the unique energy and angular relationships between the two scattered protons. Most experiments have been

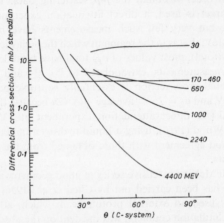

*Fig. 36. The differential cross-section for proton–proton scattering at different energies between 30 and 4400 MeV*

(Based on data collected by W. N. HESS. *Rev. Mod. Phys.* **30**, 368 (1958))

carried out using scintillation counter techniques, but some work has been done with photographic emulsions, and with hydrogen-filled diffusion chambers and bubble chambers, in which the events are relatively easy to identify.

At small centre-of-mass angles there is interference between the Coulomb scattering and the nuclear scattering. The angle at which Coulomb effects become important decreases rapidly with energy; for example at 300 MeV it is about 10° (C-system) while at 1 GeV it is 1–2°. A typical experiment is that of Fischer and Goldhaber (1954) at 330 MeV, who used photographic emulsions to detect the protons scattered from a target of liquid hydrogen. These authors found strong destructive interference between the Coulomb scattering and the nuclear scattering.

Between 100 and 350 MeV the differential cross-section for elastic nuclear scattering is found to be isotropic. At 400 MeV deviations from isotropy begin to appear at the small angles and this anisotropy becomes more marked as the bombarding energy rises (e.g. see Mescheryakov et al., 1956). This feature is illustrated in Fig. 36, which shows the data from different laboratories at energies between 70 MeV and 4400 MeV. Full references to this data can be found in the articles by Taylor (1957) and by Lindenbaum (1957).

*The elastic and inelastic scattering cross-sections for proton–proton scattering*

The total elastic cross-section can be obtained from the integration, over all angles, of the measured differential cross-sections. In the case of visual techniques this cross-section can be obtained from the total number of events found, together with a knowledge of the effective path length of incident proton track which has been searched. In cloud-chamber work the latter quantity is sometimes difficult to measure accurately and it is usual to assume a value for the total cross-section from counter work, and to derive the elastic and inelastic cross-sections from the measured ratio of elastic to inelastic events. The values of the total elastic cross-section, obtained by all these different methods, are plotted as a function of energy in Fig. 37. The subtraction of this data from the total cross-sections (Fig. 34) yields the cross-section for the pion production processes as a function of energy; this is also shown in Fig. 37.

The elastic cross-section appears to decrease slowly with increasing energy; at 6·15 GeV the measured value is $8 \pm 1$ mb (Cork et al., 1957). On the other hand, the inelastic cross-section appears to be constant, within the experimental errors, between 800 and 2600 MeV. The latter figure is the highest energy at which detailed

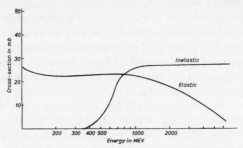

*Fig. 37. The proton–proton elastic and inelastic scattering cross-sections as a function of energy*

(Largely taken from data quoted by CHEN *et al. Phys. Rev.* **103,** 211 (1956))

measurements are available. The characteristics of the various pion production processes, which constitute the inelastic cross-section, will be discussed in the next chapter.

## Neutron–neutron scattering and charge symmetry

If charge symmetry is valid then the scattering of neutrons by neutrons should be equal to proton–proton scattering except at small angles where the Coulomb effects are significant. The first experiment to investigate *n–n* scattering at high energies was carried out by Dzhelepov *et al.* (1956b) in 1954 who made a $D_2O - H_2O$ difference experiment using 300 MeV neutrons from the Dubna 660 MeV synchrocyclotron. In terms of differential cross-sections we may write

$$\sigma_{nd}(\theta) = \sigma_{nn}(\theta) + \sigma_{np}(\theta) + I(\theta)$$

where $I(\theta)$ represents an interference term. Dzhelepov *et al.* estimated that for $E_n = 300$ MeV and $\theta = 50°$ (*C*-system) $I(\theta)$ does not exceed 15% of $\sigma_{np}$ at the same angle. At larger angles and primary energies $I(\theta)$ decreases sharply. Thus for $\theta > 50°$, it can be neglected. The experiment is not easy to perform due to (*a*) the low efficiency of neutron detectors and (*b*) the low flux of neutrons available

($\sim 10^4/cm^2$.sec at the target). The mean result from two different methods was $\sigma_{nn}(\theta) = 3\cdot7 \pm 0\cdot6$ mb/sterad from 50–90° ($C$-system) and $\sigma_{nn}$ total $= 22 \pm 5$ mb, to be compared with $\sigma_{pp}(\theta) = 3\cdot6$ mb/sterad and $\sigma_{pp}$ total $= 23$ mb, at the same energy. A similar experiment has been carried out at 590 MeV by the same group (1956a, b) using $D_2O$, $H_2O$, $CH_2$ and C targets placed in turn in the neutron beam. $I(\theta)$ was estimated to be negligible for $\theta > 30°$ ($C$-system). Good agreement was found with the corresponding $p$–$p$ results of Chen et al. (1956). These results are therefore strong evidence for the charge symmetry of nuclear forces at small distances, that is, corresponding to large angles of scatter. Further evidence for charge symmetry is provided by the equality (within the experimental errors) of the $n$–$d$ and $p$–$d$ total cross-sections at different energies. Table 10 shows some typical results taken from both American and Russian work.

### TABLE 10

| $E\,(MeV)$ | $\sigma_{nd}^{tot}\,(in\ mb)$ | $\sigma_{pd}^{tot}\,(in\ mb)$ |
|---|---|---|
| 315 | — | $56\cdot8 \pm 5$ |
| 380 | $57\cdot5 \pm 2\cdot5$ | — |
| 400 | — | $58\cdot9 \pm 1\cdot6$ |
| 500 | $65 \pm 2\cdot5$ | $61\cdot7 \pm 3\cdot0$ |
| 590 | $72 \pm 2\cdot5$ | $66\cdot8 \pm 2\cdot3$ |
| 1400 | $84\cdot6 \pm 2\cdot5$ | — |
| 1480 | — | $80\cdot8 \pm 2\cdot5$ |

## Polarization phenomena in nucleon–nucleon scattering

The production of polarized proton beams has been described in the previous chapter, together with an account of some of the work on the scattering of polarized protons by complex nuclei. Nucleon–nucleon scattering using polarized beams has been the subject of much experimental work. Before beams of polarized nucleons became available, only the differential and total cross-sections could be measured. These data do not contain sufficient information to allow the determination of the phase shifts for nucleon–nucleon scattering. A partial wave analysis of these data still allow a continuous infinity of solutions for the phase shifts. Experiments with polarized nucleon beams determine further combinations of the

phase shifts. In the case of proton–proton scattering at 300 MeV, it
has proved possible to determine experimentally sufficient different
combinations of the phase shifts to limit those for proton–proton
scattering to eight possible sets.

## p–p experiments

The scattering of polarized protons from hydrogen to determine
$P(\theta)$ has been studied at a number of energies between 140 and 635
MeV. The experimental arrangement used is similar to that described for the studies of $P(\theta)$ for complex nuclei (e.g. Fig. 31); a
typical paper, which gives a detailed account of the work carried out
at Berkeley, is that of Chamberlain *et al.* (1957). It is most convenient
to express the data in terms of the product $P(\theta) \, d\sigma/d\Omega$ of the
unpolarized differential cross-section $d\sigma/d\Omega$ and the measured
polarization $P(\theta)$. It can be shown that this product has an angular
dependence of the form

$$P(\theta)\frac{d\sigma}{d\Omega} = \sin\theta\cos\theta[a + b\cos^2\theta + c\cos^4\theta + \ldots] \quad (7.1)$$

The odd powers of $\cos\theta$ are missing in the term in square brackets
because the two particles are identical. If only $S$ and $P$ waves participate in the scattering, this expression reduces to

$$P(\theta)\frac{d\sigma}{d\Omega} = a\sin\theta\cos\theta \quad (7.2)$$

The $\cos^2\theta$ term arises from interference between the scattering
from the $^3P$ and the $^3F$ states. There is no contribution from the $D$
states to the expression for $P(\theta) \, d\sigma/d\Omega$ for (a) the $^3D$ states are
forbidden for identical particles by the Pauli principle, and (b) the
singlet $^1D$ states (anti-parallel spins) cannot give rise to any polarization. Singlet states do not contribute to the polarization owing to
the spherical symmetry of a singlet spin state, the spins of the two
nucleons being coupled to zero total spin, a situation with complete
rotational symmetry. In a singlet state there can therefore be no
preferred direction for the spin of either of the outgoing protons,
so that each of the outgoing proton beams is necessarily unpolarized
in singlet state scattering. Observation of a $\cos^2\theta$ term in the expression (7.1) for $P(\theta) \, d\sigma/d\Omega$ would therefore show at once that
$F$ waves are participating in the scattering. This has been found,

for example, in the results obtained at 95 MeV by a group at Harvard.

More information is obtained from measurements of the angular dependence of the various triple scattering parameters such as $D$ and $R$. Such experiments become rather difficult at energies lower than 100 MeV since the energy of the scattered beam becomes too low for any analyser to give measurable asymmetries. The most complete information available in 1958 was at an energy of ∼300 MeV. Valuable information can also be obtained from measurements in the small-angle region, where there is interference between the Coulomb scattering and the nuclear scattering.

*n–p experiments*

Polarization experiments using neutrons are rather more difficult than those using protons. The neutron beams used usually have an appreciable energy spread, while the neutron detectors employed have a low efficiency. Further, the polarization of most of the neutron beams has been low so that in a double scattering experiment the asymmetries to be measured are small. Experiments have been carried out at energies between 77 and 600 MeV, while a *p*-'*n*' experiment using polarized protons has been performed at 300 MeV.

In the present case the product $P(\theta)\, d\sigma/d\Omega$ can be expressed in the form

$$P(\theta)\frac{d\sigma}{d\Omega} = \sin\theta[a + b\cos\theta + c\cos^2\theta + \ldots] \qquad (7.3)$$

which includes all powers of $\cos\theta$, since the scattering particles are now not identical. For $S$ and $P$ waves only (7.3) reduces to

$$P(\theta)\frac{d\sigma}{d\Omega} = \sin\theta[a + b\cos\theta] \qquad (7.4)$$

and the $\cos^2\theta$ term arises first from interference between $D$-waves and $P$-waves. At 95 MeV the experimental data requires the $\cos^2\theta$ term, while at 330 MeV the $\cos^3\theta$ term is important.

## Analysis and interpretation of the data

The nucleon–nucleon interaction, which involves the intermediary pion field, is difficult to describe in basic field theory terms. It is only recently that field theory has been able to give a reasonable account of pion–nucleon scattering, and of the photoproduction of pions from nucleons, at low energies. It is unlikely, therefore, that a theory of the nucleon–nucleon interaction, satisfactory at all energies, will be formulated in the immediate future. At the present time it is usual to analyse the data in terms of the isotopic spin states which participate in the scattering, and in terms of the phase shifts derived from a partial wave analysis. The next step is to calculate a potential which will reproduce the experimental data over a wide energy range; this stage was reached in 1957. The final problem is the formulation of a field theory which will yield such potentials.

*Isotopic spin states*

The different elastic scattering reactions for neutrons and protons are:

(1) $p + p \rightarrow p + p$    Antisymmetric states ⎫
(2) $n + n \rightarrow n + n$    Antisymmetric states ⎪ in space and
(3) $n + p \rightarrow n + p$    Antisymmetric states ⎬ ordinary spin
(4) $n + p \rightarrow n + p$    Symmetric states ⎭

The assumption of charge symmetry means, in terms of cross-sections, that (1) = (2); the further assumption of charge independence means that (1) = (2) = (3). Thus only two scattering amplitudes need be considered, those involving the symmetric and antisymmetric states in the space and spin variables, or the $T = 0$ and $T = 1$ isotopic spin states respectively. These assumptions considerably simplify the analysis of the data.

The clearest evidence for charge independence at high energies is provided by experiments involving pion production. In nucleon–nucleon scattering the hypothesis leads only to certain inequalities between various cross-sections. In particular

$$4\sigma_{np}(\theta = \pi/2) \geqslant \sigma_{pp}(\theta = \pi/2) \qquad (7.5)$$

and $$\sqrt{\sigma_{np}(\theta = 0)} + \sqrt{\sigma_{np}(\theta = \pi)} \geqslant \sqrt{\sigma_{pp}(\theta = 0)} \qquad (7.6)$$

All the data that are at present available are consistent with all the inequalities that may be written down, although the errors are still large in some cases.

Now the $n$–$p$ system is an equal mixture of $T = 0$ and $T = 1$ states while the $p$–$p$ system corresponds to a $T = 1$ state only. In terms of total cross-sections

$$\sigma_{np} = \tfrac{1}{2}\sigma(T=0) + \tfrac{1}{2}\sigma(T=1)$$

and since     $\sigma(T=1) = \sigma_{pp}$

then          $\sigma(T=0) = 2\sigma_{np} - \sigma_{pp}$          (7.7)

It is therefore possible to derive $\sigma(T=0)$ as a function of energy from the $np$ and $pp$ total cross-section curves. The result is shown in Fig. 38, together with the $\sigma_{pp}(T=1)$ curve. The curves are similar

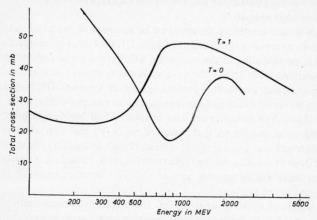

*Fig. 38. The cross-sections for nucleon–nucleon scattering in the $T=0$ and $T=1$ states, as a function of energy*

(Based on data quoted by CHEN *et al. Phys. Rev.* **103**, 211 (1956) )

in shape but are displaced relative to each other in energy by about 700 MeV. A possible explanation, in terms of pion production, of this feature of the data above 400 MeV, will be considered in the next chapter. Below this energy the collisions are predominantly elastic and it is clear that there is a marked difference in the scattering in the two states. This is confirmed by a study of the energy and angular dependence of the total and differential cross-sections for $T=0$ and $T=1$ states. The differential cross-sections can be obtained from the relations

$$2[\sigma_{np}(\theta) + \sigma_{np}(\pi - \theta)] - \sigma_{pp}(\theta) = \sigma_{T=0}(\theta) \qquad (7.8)$$

and                                    $\sigma_{pp}(\theta) = \sigma_{T=1}(\theta)$          (7.9)

For example, at 300 MeV $\sigma_{T=0}(\theta)$, as a function of angle, is strongly peaked in the forward direction, while $\sigma_{T=1}(\theta)$ is isotropic. Further examples are given in a paper by Dzhelepov *et al.* (1956b), which presents much of the Russian work between 460 and 660 MeV.

This analysis in terms of isotopic spin states is, of course, phenomenological in character, but is particularly valuable in that it distinguishes particular features of the experimental data.

*Phase-shift analysis*

Any elastic scattering process can be analysed in terms of partial waves, as we have discussed in Chapter III. Each angular momentum state participating in the scattering will have a certain phase shift associated with it. For the case of nucleon–nucleon scattering the approximate classical argument, given in Chapter III, suggests that waves of $l \leqslant 2$ must be considered at energies of the order of 20 MeV. The polarization data at around 140 MeV confirms this suggestion and shows that waves of $l = 3$ ($F$) make an important contribution at this energy. It is clear, therefore, that any phase-shift analysis of the data will be quite complex, and, further, it is unlikely that there will be enough data of sufficient accuracy to result in a unique set of phase shifts.

Many phase-shift analyses of the nucleon–nucleon scattering data have been made. We shall mention only one here in order to illustrate the complexity of the problem, that of Stapp *et al.* (1957), who have made an extensive analysis of all the Berkeley data at 310 MeV. These authors took 36 experimental measurements of $p$–$p$ scattering at ~310 MeV as a starting point for their analysis; these were the total cross-section, the differential cross-section at 14 angles (including 4 in the Coulomb interference region), the polarization of 6 angles, values of $D$ at 6 angles, of $R$ at 6 angles, and of $A$ at 3 angles. This data overdetermines the problem, for it can be shown that the number of phase shifts required to describe the $p$–$p$ scattering is $\frac{5}{2}l_{max} + \frac{3}{2}$ for $l_{max}$ odd and $\frac{5}{2}l_{max}$ for $l_{max}$ even, while the experiments can yield $8l_{max} + 4$ independent parameters; $l_{max}$ is the maximum value of $l$ contributing to the scattering. The analysis of Stapp *et al.* considered waves up to $l = 5$ ($H$ waves), and was carried out using electronic computers. Eight best sets of phase shifts were found; three of these were found to be incompatible with the data derived from a study of the reaction $p + p \longrightarrow \pi^+ + d$. The remaining five sets have several common characteristics; all have negative $^1S_0$ phase shifts and positive $^1D_2$ and $^1G_4$ phase shifts. This suggests that in the singlet state there is a repulsive hard core surrounded by an attractive potential. In the triplet states the $^3P_0$ and $^3P_1$ phase shifts are negative while the $^3P_2$ phase shifts are large and positive.

The available $n$–$p$ data was not used in making this analysis. Application of this information, together with the principle of charge independence, and the use of dispersion relations, may possibly provide a means of reducing the number of solutions which describe the data. Polarization experiments on the analysis in coincidence of both the scattered protons, from unpolarized protons incident on hydrogen, will also yield more detailed information, which may enable some of the remaining phase shifts to be rejected.

*Potentials*

It is natural to try to express the interaction between two nucleons in terms of a potential, that is, in terms of their interaction energy. The simplest assumption is that this depends only on the distance between the particles as is often the case for classical systems (e.g. the Coulomb potential). Such a force is sometimes known as a Wigner force. Since the nucleons have both spin and isotopic spin their interaction energy may also depend on these variables. It is conventional to express this dependence in terms of operators which exchange the spin, the charge (isotopic spin), or both the spin and the charge of the particles. The last is equivalent to leaving the spin and charge alone and interchanging only the space co-ordinates of the two nucleons; it is sometimes known as the Majorana interaction, and has the same effect as the parity operation. A Majorana interaction thus gives rise to an ordinary potential which changes sign according to whether $l$ is odd or even and is independent of spin. All these interactions are of an exchange character, but forces of this type are not known in classical physics. They are, however, well known in molecular physics, where their origin is of a purely quantum-mechanical nature; for example, the forces between two atoms giving a molecule with homopolar binding are of an exchange character, due to an exchange effect involving the electrons of the two atoms.

The forces mentioned above are all central interactions, that is they depend only on the distance between the two particles and not on the direction of their relative position vector. Non-central interactions may also occur. The tensor potential is the only one which does not vanish in the low-energy limit; this depends on the relative orientation of the total spin and the line joining the two particles. The existence of a tensor component in nuclear forces is known from the properties of the deuteron, from its quadrupole moment and magnetic moment. Another simple non-central potential is the spin-orbit potential $(\sigma_1 + \sigma_2)\mathbf{L}.V(r)$ which couples the total spin $(\sigma_1 + \sigma_2)$ of the two particles with their orbital angular momentum $\mathbf{L}$; this depends not only on the positions but also on the momenta of the particles.

Whatever the potential written down, when it is included in the Schrödinger equation representing the two particles, it should correctly determine their motion. For example, the Wigner interaction predicts that when two nucleons collide the scattering will be predominantly in the forward direction (in the $C$-system) and will become increasingly peaked forward as the bombarding energy increases. An exchange interaction of the Majorana type would give rise to pronounced backward scattering in the $C$-system, for the effect of the interaction is for the two particles to exchange their positions in space.

*Experimental evidence for the different potentials*

The well-known saturation of nuclear forces cannot be explained in terms of an ordinary Wigner potential, attractive at all distances and independent of the angular momentum. A tensor force also is not sufficient to give saturation, independent of its sign. A potential is required which prevents the particles from getting too close to each other. There are three possibilities

(1) A potential representing exchange forces such as those that have been discussed previously.

(2) A potential which is repulsive at short distances.

(3) Many body forces.

Direct evidence for strong exchange forces is provided by the $n$–$p$ differential scattering cross-section curves of Fig. 37. Above 50 MeV there is a very high probability that the neutron emerges from the interaction in the backward direction in the $C$-system of the two colliding particles. The change in the character of the $n$–$p$ angular distribution between 380 and 580 MeV is a reflection of the fact that pion production becomes increasingly important between these energies. This means that absorption is taking place so that the effective potential between the nucleons becomes complex; as a consequence the elastic scattering are largely diffraction scattering, which is peaked in the forward direction. The exchange forces, of course, still give rise to appreciable scattering in the backward direction.

The main features to be explained in $p$–$p$ scattering between 100 and 400 MeV are the constancy and isotropic nature of the elastic differential cross-section. The scattering would be isotropic if only $S$-waves contributed; the maximum cross-section is then given by equation (3.34) when $\sin \delta = 1$. This gives a value of $d\sigma/d\Omega$ of 2·5 mb/steradian, much lower than the experimental value of $3·6 \pm 0·2$ mb/steradian. This magnitude can be explained only by invoking waves of $l = 1$; the isotropy of the scattering is then presumably the result of a special combination of different angular momentum states. The striking polarization data requires, of course, first that large contributions are made by waves of odd angular momentum particularly $l = 1$ and $l = 3$, and secondly that there must be a strong component of non-central force in the nucleon–nucleon interaction.

The near isotropy of $d\sigma/d\Omega$ rules out potentials for which the phase shifts in states of successively higher $l$ have the same sign, but isotropy can be obtained by alternate negative and positive phase shifts with increasing $l$. A change of sign between $S$ and $D$ waves, for example, may result from a strongly repulsive core in addition to the attractive potential. The $S$-wave phase shift will depend on this central core and will become negative at high energies. The higher $l$-waves will be kept away from the core by centrifugal forces and will have the normal positive phase shifts corresponding to an ordinary attractive potential. All the phase shift solutions of Stapp *et al.* at 300 MeV have these features. Certain features of pion–proton scattering experiments at energies above 1 GeV and of the optical model for high-energy scattering, are best explained in terms of the repulsive core hypothesis. There is some indication of such an effect from the meson theory of nuclear forces.

The qualitative features of the nucleon–nucleon scattering data give evidence for exchange forces and for the existence of a repulsive potential at small distances. A number of potential models containing these features have been employed in an attempt to predict the phase shifts derived from a detailed partial wave analysis of the data. None of the models employing only central and tensor energy-independent potentials has been successful in fitting the data. Recently attempts have been made to include a short-range spin-orbit force in the nucleon–nucleon interaction, with quite promising results. For example Gammel and Thaler (1957a) took a potential of the form

$$V(r) = V_1(r) + V_T(r)S_{12} + V_{LS}(r)\,\boldsymbol{\sigma}.\mathbf{L} \qquad (7.10)$$

where $V_T$ is the tensor potential and $S_{12}$ is the tensor operator. It was assumed that all three potentials had a general spin and parity dependence, but that they were energy-independent. Gammel and Thaler showed that a potential of this form could reproduce all the $p$–$p$ data below 310 MeV and, moreover, the phase shifts calculated from this potential were very close to those of solution 1 of Stapp *et al.* at 310 MeV. Assuming the nucleon–nucleon interaction to be charge-independent, and using a similar spin-orbit potential, Gammel and Thaler (1957b) were also able to obtain a reasonable fit to the $n$–$p$ scattering and polarization data at 90, 150 and 310 MeV. Signell and Marshak (1957) have independently obtained similar results for $p$–$p$ and $n$–$p$ scattering between 40 and 150 MeV.

At the present time it is clear that there is good evidence for (i) exchange interactions; (ii) strong non-central forces including both tensor forces (required for the low-energy, and deuteron, data) and short-range spin-orbit forces (to account for the large polarizations observed); and (iii) a strong repulsive core. Potentials of the general form of (7.10) appear to give a good representation of the data, but the basic problem, that of calculating such potentials from a suitable field theory of the pion, and possibly of other mesonic particles, remains.

## Elastic scattering above 400 MeV

At energies above the threshold for pion production the analysis of the data becomes more difficult, since the presence of absorption must be represented by a complex potential. On the other hand a simple optical model gives results in good agreement with the data. The marked anistropy and forward peaking of the differential elastic $p–p$ scattering, which appears above 400 MeV, suggests that at energies of the order of 1 GeV the target proton may appear as an absorbing sphere to the incident proton wave. Thus the elastic scattering may be regarded as diffraction scattering (Serber and Rarita, 1955). At energies above 1 GeV the elastic scattering cross-section, and the total cross-section, both decrease in a marked manner, while the pion production cross-section remains approximately constant with increasing nucleon energy. Brown (1958) has shown that these features of the data can be reproduced by a model which assumes that at 1 GeV the proton–proton scattering can be analysed in terms of an interaction which is taken to be confined to a hard core of radius $0·45 \times 10^{-13}$ cm, together with an external region of absorption of Gaussian form. The hard core is assumed to disappear with increasing energy and to be replaced by absorption. This model also predicts the shape of the curves of the differential cross-section, which are in reasonable accord with the experimental data, both at 1 GeV and at 6 GeV.

## BIBLIOGRAPHY

BETHE, H. A. and MORRISON, P. 1956. *Elementary Nuclear Theory*. 2nd Ed. Ch. 15, 16. John Wiley, New York.

BLATT, J. M. and WEISSKOPF, V. F. 1952. *Theoretical Nuclear Physics*. Ch. 3, 4. Chapman & Hall, London.

LINDENBAUM, S. J. 1957. *Ann Rev. Nuc. Sci.* **7**, 317.

TAYLOR, A. E. 1957. *Reports on Progress in Physics*, **20**, 86.

## REFERENCES

BATSON, A. P., CULWICK, B. B., KLEPP, H. and RIDDIFORD, L. 1959. *Proc. Roy. Soc.* **251**, 233.

BROWN, G. E. 1958. *Phys. Rev.* **111**, 1178.

CHAMBERLAIN, O., SEGRÈ, E., TRIPP, R. D., WIEGAND, C. and YPSILANTIS, T. 1957. *Phys. Rev.* **105**, 288.

CHEN, F. F., LEAVITT, C. P. and SHAPIRO, A. M. 1956. *Phys. Rev.* **103**, 211.

COOR, T. A., HILL, D. A., HORNYAK, W. F., SMITH, L. W. and SNOW, G. A. 1955. *Phys. Rev.* **98**, 1369.

CORK, B., WENZEL, W. A. and CAUSEY, C. W. 1957. *Phys. Rev.* **107**, 859.

DZHELEPOV, V. P., GOLOVIN, B. M., KAZARINOV, YU. M. and SIMONOV, N. N. 1956a. *CERN Symposium*, **II**, 115.

DZHELEPOV, V. P., KAZARINOV, YU. M., GOLOVIN, B. M., FLYAGIN, V. B. and SATAROV, V. I. 1956b. *Nuovo Cimento*, **III**, Supplemento No. 1, 61.

FISCHER, D. and GOLDHABER, G. 1954. *Phys. Rev.* **95**, 1350.

GAMMEL, J. L. and THALER, R. M. 1957a. *Phys. Rev.* **107**, 291; 1957b. ibid. **107**, 1337.

MESCHERYAKOV, M. G., BOGACHEV, N. P., LEKSIN, G. A., NEGANOV, B. S. and PISKAREV, E. V. 1956. *CERN Symposium*, **II**, 125.

NEDZEL, V. A. 1954. *Phys. Rev.* **94**, 174.

SERBER, R. and RARITA, W. 1955. *Phys. Rev.* **99**, 629(A).

SIGNELL, P. S. and MARSHAK, R. E. 1957. *Phys. Rev.* **106**, 832.

STAPP, H. P., YPSILANTIS, T., and METROPOLIS, N. 1957. *Phys. Rev.* **105**, 302.

TAYLOR, A. E. and WOOD, E. 1956. *Proc. Phys. Soc.* **A69**, 645.

# CHAPTER VIII

# Pion Production
# in Nucleon–Nucleon Collisions

---

## Introduction

It is found experimentally that there is a finite chance that a pion will be produced whenever sufficient energy is available in the $C$-system of two colliding nucleons. The cross-section for pion production rises rapidly as the available energy increases and the magnitude of the cross-section is large. This fact is consistent with the hypothesis that the pion is the meson largely responsible for nuclear forces. For a proton striking another proton at rest the threshold energy for charged pion production is 296 MeV in the laboratory system. For protons incident on complex nuclei the threshold energy can be as low as 170 MeV, for the target protons and neutrons can have appreciable Fermi energies. In this chapter we shall consider only pion production in nucleon–nucleon collisions, and will, for the most part, restrict our remarks to proton–proton collisions. Relatively little information is available about pion production in neutron–proton collisions, largely due to the difficulty of obtaining sufficiently intense, monoenergetic neutron beams. Further, in the case of both neutral and positive pion production in $n$–$p$ collisions, two of the three final state particles are electrically neutral, and are therefore difficult to detect. On the other hand, for pion production in proton–proton collisions extensive information is available from threshold up to 450 MeV from the work with the synchrocyclotrons in the U.S.A., and to 660 MeV from the work carried out with the Russian synchrocyclotron at Dubna. Above 660 MeV limited data is available from experiments with the relatively weak beams from the proton synchrotrons, and mostly using the visual techniques.

The threshold energy for double pion production in nucleon–nucleon collisions is about 590 MeV, but the measured cross-section is small up to about 1 GeV. It is therefore convenient for us to consider first, and in some detail, the single pion production processes, up to about 700 MeV incident nucleon energy. The higher energy data will be briefly discussed in the latter part of this chapter. We have remarked earlier (p. 140) on the difficulties which beset any field theoretical approach to the problem of nucleon–nucleon scattering. The elastic scattering data were analysed and discussed in terms of phenomenological ideas; similarly the pion production data are, at the present time, best discussed in phenomenological terms. We begin, therefore, with a brief explanation of this approach.

## Phenomenological description of pion production

Very soon after the first studies of pion production near threshold had been carried out, Watson and Brueckner pointed out that the characteristics of the data could be simply interpreted in terms of a partial wave analysis, with only a few angular momentum states to be considered. This approach, based on the laws of conservation of angular momentum and parity, has been extended and compared with experiment by Rosenfeld (1954) and Gell-Mann and Watson (1954).

For proton–proton collisions there are three possible reactions which lead to single pion production, viz.:

$$p + p \longrightarrow n + p + \pi^+ \tag{8.1}$$

$$p + p \longrightarrow d + \pi^+ \tag{8.2}$$

$$p + p \longrightarrow p + p + \pi^0 \tag{8.3}$$

Suppose that the kinetic energy of the incident proton is about 400 MeV. In the $C$-system, the available energy is about 210 MeV; of this 140 MeV is taken by the rest mass of the created pion, leaving 70 MeV to be shared amongst the final state particles. Very roughly the pion takes about 55 MeV on the average and the two nucleons about 15 MeV. It is reasonable to suppose, therefore, that the two final state nucleons will be in an $S$-state relative to each other; the probability of formation of this state is high because of the known strong attractive interaction between two nucleons in a

$^1S_0$ state, and, for a neutron and a proton, also in the $^3S_1$ state. The further assumption is made that the created pion is either in an $s$-state or a $p$-state with respect to the centre of mass of the whole system. The four possible transitions yielding pions may then be written as

$$^3P_1 \longrightarrow {}^3S_1 s_1 \tag{8.4}$$

$$^1S_0 \longrightarrow {}^3S_1 p_0 \tag{8.5}$$

$$^1D_2 \longrightarrow {}^3S_1 p_2 \tag{8.6}$$

$$^3P_0 \longrightarrow {}^1S_0 s_0 \tag{8.7}$$

The initial state of the two colliding nucleons is given on the left-hand side, using the usual terminology of $^{2S+1}L_J$; on the right-hand side the final state of the two nucleons is given first, followed by a small letter to express the orbital angular momentum of the pion, while the final subscript is the total angular momentum $J$. These transitions are often simply called $Ss$ and $Sp$ transitions, and they are the only ones allowed by the conservation laws. For example, consider (8.5) and (8.6); the final nucleons have $l = 0$ (basic assumption) and even parity, while the pion has $l = 1$, and for a $^3S_1$ state of the nucleons, can combine with them to give a total $J$ value for the system of 0, 1 or 2. The parity will be even, remembering that the pion has negative intrinsic parity. The only initial nucleon states of even parity, which also conserve $J$, are the $^1S_0$ and $^1D_2$ states; the $^3P_1$ state has odd parity, while the singlet $P$ state is forbidden by the Pauli principle. Therefore, for $Sp$ transitions, only (8.5) and (8.6) are allowed.

All the four transitions given above contribute to positive pion production together with nucleons. In the case of pion production with a deuteron only the first three transitions are possible; the fourth is forbidden for the deuteron spin is one. On the other hand, it is only the fourth that is allowed for neutral pion production, for the $^3S_1$ state is forbidden to the two final state protons by the Pauli principle. If the angular momentum states participating in a given reaction are defined, it is possible, in simple cases, to derive the expected angular distribution of the pions. If the total angular momentum, $J = 0$, or if the pion is produced in an $s$-state, then the distribution will be isotropic. If the meson is produced in a $p$-state and if $J \geqslant 1$, the angular distribution can be shown to be of the form $C + \cos^2 \theta$; if the states are perfectly definite then the value of $C$ can be calculated. For example, for the transition $^1D_2 \longrightarrow {}^3S_1 p_2$ the angular distribution is $\frac{1}{3} + \cos^2 \theta$.

A broader classification may be made in terms of the isotopic spin states of the initial and final nucleons. For proton–proton collisions the initial state is always a $T = 1$ state; in the final state the two nucleons may have $T = 0$ or $T = 1$, except when they are two protons, when again only $T = 1$ is allowed. Thus the cross-section for the sum of the reactions (8.1) and (8.2) may be written as $\sigma_{10} + \sigma_{11}$, whereas that for (8.3) may be written as $\sigma_{11}$; the first suffix gives the isotopic spin state of the initial nucleons and the second that of the final nucleons (Table 11). The cross-section for

## TABLE 11

| Process | Cross-section |
|---|---|
| $p + p \longrightarrow n + p + \pi^+$ | $\sigma_{10} + \sigma_{11}$ |
| $p + p \longrightarrow d + \pi^+$ | $\sigma_{10}(D)$ |
| $p + p \longrightarrow p + p + \pi^0$ | $\sigma_{11}$ |
| $n + p \longrightarrow \pi^{\pm} + \text{nucleons}$ | $\frac{1}{2}(\sigma_{11} + \sigma_{01})$ |
| $n + p \longrightarrow \pi^0 + \text{nucleons}$ | $\frac{1}{2}(\sigma_{10} + \sigma_{01})$ |
| $n + p \longrightarrow \pi^0 + d$ | $\frac{1}{2}(\sigma_{10}(D))$ |

reaction (8.2) only may be written as $\sigma_{10}(D)$, for the isotopic spin of a deuteron is zero. The same considerations may be applied to pion production in neutron–proton collisions and the corresponding expressions are given in the latter half of the table. The cross-section $\sigma_{01}$ appears in this case because the initial neutron–proton system is equally composed of $T = 0$ and $T = 1$ isotopic spin states. The cross-section $\sigma_{00}$ does not arise, for it cannot conserve isotopic spin. All these relations are derived using the hypothesis of charge independence, and neglect the difference in mass between the charged and neutral pions.

We may conveniently summarize in Table 12 the essential features of the phenomenological analysis that we have discussed. Under $\sigma_{11}$ all the possible $Pp$ and $Ps$ transitions have been written down, for these are of importance in the discussion of neutral pion production.

## TABLE 12

| Isotopic reaction | Class | Initial state | Final state | Angular distribution |
|---|---|---|---|---|
| $\sigma_{10}$ | $Ss$ | $^3P_1$ | $^3S_1s_1$ | Isotropic |
| | $Sp$ | $^1S_0$ | $^3S_1p_0$ | Isotropic |
| | | $^1D_2$ | $^3S_1p_2$ | $\frac{1}{3} + \cos^2\theta$ |
| $\sigma_{01}$ | $Sp$ | $\left.\begin{array}{c}^3S_1 \\ ^3D_1\end{array}\right\}$ | $^1S_0p_1$ | $\left\{\begin{array}{l}\text{Isotropic} \\ \frac{1}{3} + \cos^2\theta\end{array}\right.$ |
| $\sigma_{11}$ | $Ss$ | $^3P_0$ | $^1S_0s_0$ | Isotropic |
| | $Sp$ | none | | |
| | $Pp$ | $^3P_{0,1}$ | $\left.\begin{array}{c}^3P_0p_1 \\ ^3P_1p_{0,1,2} \\ ^3P_2p_{1,2,3}\end{array}\right\}$ | $C + \cos^2\theta$ |
| | | $^3P_{0,1,2}$ or $^3F_2$ | | |
| | | $^3P_{1,2}$ or $^3F_{2,3}$ | | |
| | $Ps$ | $^1S_0$ | $^3P_0s_0$ | Isotropic |
| | | $^1D_2$ | $^3P_2s_2$ | Isotropic |

### The pion–nucleon resonant state

The scattering experiments discussed in Chapters IV and V indicate that the $T = \frac{3}{2}$, $J = \frac{3}{2}$ state of a pion and a nucleon is one of particularly strong attractive interaction. One may well expect this interaction to play an important role in meson production processes in which a pion and one, or more, nucleons are in the final state. This point was first considered by Brueckner and Watson (1952), who used it to give a qualitative reason for the experimentally small value of $\sigma_{01}$. The argument was the following. Assume that pion emission takes place in two stages; first one of the colliding nucleons is raised to a virtual excited state of $J = \frac{3}{2}$, $T = \frac{3}{2}$ (i.e. $l_\pi = 1$). The energy for this excitation comes from the kinetic energy of the relative motion of the two nucleons. In the second stage of the process the excited nucleon is assumed to decay into a nucleon and a pion. In symbols

$$\left.\begin{array}{c}N + N \longrightarrow (N^* + N) \\ N^* \longrightarrow N + \pi\end{array}\right\} \qquad (8.8a)$$

and

Thus, in the intermediate state, enclosed in brackets in (8.8a), the excited nucleon, $N^*$, has $T = \frac{3}{2}$ while the remaining nucleon has $T = \frac{1}{2}$. The total isotopic spin is therefore 1 or 2. The initial nucleon state can only have $T = 1$ if it is composed of two protons, and 0 or 1 if it is a neutron and a proton. It is clear that the transition represented by $\sigma_{01}$ cannot give rise to the excited state under discussion, for it cannot conserve isotopic spin. We might therefore expect $\sigma_{01}$ to be small, if the excited state plays an important role.

The hypothesis that pion production takes place predominantly through the $T = J = \frac{3}{2}$ pion–nucleon state is a possible explanation for the energy characteristics of the total cross-section curves for scattering in the $T = 0$ and $T = 1$ states (Fig. 38). The $T = 1$ cross-section rises as soon as the single pion production energy threshold is reached, since it can lead to a $T = \frac{3}{2}$ pion–nucleon state. The $T = 0$ state cannot do this, and thus the cross-section for scattering in the $T = 0$ state remains approximately constant until the energy threshold for double pion production is reached. Then pion production can take place via

$$\left.\begin{array}{l} N + N \longrightarrow N^* + N^* \\ N^* \longrightarrow N + \pi \end{array}\right\} \qquad (8.8b)$$

and each

and now $T = 0$ states can contribute to (8.8b) for each $N^*$ will have $T = \frac{3}{2}$, which can combine together to give a total $T = 0$. Thus the cross-section for scattering from $T = 0$ states rises, corresponding to pion production through reaction (8.8b).

A consideration of Table 12 shows that for $\sigma_{10}$ only the $^1D_2 \longrightarrow {}^3S_1p_2$ transition can give rise to a virtual $T = J = \frac{3}{2}$ excited state; the total angular momentum must be $\frac{3}{2} \pm \frac{1}{2}$ so that the $^1S_0 \longrightarrow {}^3S_1p_0$ transition is not allowed. For $\sigma_{11}$ any of the $Pp$ transitions can proceed via the excited state. We might expect, therefore, that these particular reactions would be enhanced at the expense of the others, if the resonance state is of importance.

The suggestion that the meson–nucleon resonant state dominated the pion production process was made by Lindenbaum and Yuan (1953). These authors measured the energy spectra of the pions emitted from proton–Be collisions at $1\cdot0$ and $2\cdot3$ GeV incident proton energy. The spectra obtained (transformed to the $C$-system) were similar in shape to the graph of the $\pi^+ + p$ scattering cross-section plotted as a function of energy, and showed a characteristic peak between 100 and 200 MeV. Lindenbaum and Yuan suggested, therefore, that the pion production process took place predominantly through the excitation of one, or both, nucleons to an isobaric state of $T = J = \frac{3}{2}$ (see pp. 77–78). The excited nucleon (suppose only one is excited) is assumed to decay to a nucleon and a pion after a time which is great enough for the two nucleons to move apart, so that the nucleon–nucleon interaction can be ignored. In this form, the hypothesis is sometimes known as the 'isobar model'. It was subsequently used by Peaslee (1954) to predict $\pi^+ : \pi^- : \pi^0$ production ratios from nucleons, and from complex nuclei, at 1 GeV and at higher energies. More recently, Lindenbaum and Sternheimer (1957) have used this model to calculate the characteristics of pion production in $p$–$p$ collisions at energies ranging from 800 MeV to 3 GeV.

The first extensive analysis of the experimental data, in terms of the considerations set out in the previous section, was made by Rosenfeld (1954). He confined his attention to the energy region between the threshold for pion production and 400 MeV. His analysis showed that a substantial part of the production took place through the $^1D_2 \longrightarrow {}^3S_1p_2$ transition, which can give rise to the isobaric intermediate state. This approach has been extended to 700 MeV by Mandelstam (1958), who effectively takes the isobar picture by assuming that

(i) the outgoing pion is in a resonant $T = J = \frac{3}{2}$ state with one of the nucleons

(ii) only low angular momenta ($S$ and $P$ waves) are effective between the nucleon and the isobar in the intermediate state

and (iii) that the matrix element for each particular transition is constant *except* for factors due to the final state pion–nucleon and nucleon–nucleon interactions.

He considers the nucleon not in a resonant state to be either in an $S$-state or a $P$-state relative to the centre of mass of the isobar system. These two possibilities are called '$S$-state production' and '$P$-state production'; one parameter is associated with the former possibility and two with the latter. The $S$-state production corresponds mainly to the $^1D_2 \longrightarrow {}^3S_1p_2$ transition discussed earlier, while $P$-state production corresponds to the $Pp$ transitions as well as to part of the $Ss$ and $Sd$ transitions. The latter probabilities arise because the two nucleons may be in a relative $S$ state (to each other) even though one may be in a $P$ state with respect to the centre of mass of the isobar. The pion may be in an $s$- or a $d$-state relative to the centre of mass of the two nucleons, so the two possibilities of $Ss$ and $Sd$ exist. The $Sp$ case comes under the heading of $S$-state production in Mandelstam's terminology. The $Ss$ and $Sd$ transitions are important near the threshold. The $S$-state parameter is fixed by the cross-section for positive pion production with deuteron formation near threshold; one of the $P$-state parameters is fixed from the cross-section for $P$-state pion production with deuteron formation, and turns out to be zero, while the other is fixed from the cross-section for positive pion production without deuteron formation at 660 MeV. Using these three parameters, Mandelstam is able to obtain excellent agreement with the experimental data up to 700 MeV, except near threshold. In this region non-resonance production is important and further parameters become necessary.

## Experimental studies of pion production up to 700 MeV

### Proton–proton collisions

The three processes (8.1), (8.2) and (8.3) have been studied in considerable detail from the threshold energy up to 660 MeV. We shall first discuss the studies of positive meson production. The mesons may be detected by a scintillation counter telescope, by photographic emulsions, or in a diffusion cloud chamber in which the hydrogen gas is also the target material. The reaction involving deuteron production is readily identifiable, for it yields a positive pion and a deuteron, which are both of a unique energy for a given angle of emission. In all experiments observations are made at a series of angles, and the data is then integrated over all angles to give the total cross-section for any particular process. For example, the reactions yielding positive pions have been studied in detail by Neganov and Savchenko (1957), over a wide energy range. These authors used a counter telescope of four scintillation crystals in series to detect the pions; suitable thicknesses of copper or aluminium between the different crystals enabled the energy spectrum to be determined. Measurements were made at eight different angles. Instead of counters it is possible to use emulsions to detect the mesons. The observation of the point at which any meson stops in an emulsion gives its range in the emulsion, and therefore its energy. Thus, in an emulsion placed at a given angle to, say, a hydrogen target, the complete energy spectrum is given by the range spectrum of the mesons stopped in the emulsion. An experiment of this type has been carried out at 660 MeV by Sidorov (1957). In both experiments the pions associated with deuteron formation appear as a line spectrum at the maximum possible energy. At 383 MeV Alston *et al.* (1956) passed an intense, collimated 'pencil' beam into a hydrogen-filled diffusion chamber, and looked for positive pions originating from the beam. The actual collision is not seen in this type of experiment; only the resultant pion is observed, whose energy is derived from its curvature in the magnetic field applied across the chamber.

Neutral pion production is intrinsically more difficult to study than charged pion production, for one must observe either one, or preferably both, of the decay $\gamma$-rays. A detailed account of much of the Russian work has been published by Bayukov *et al.* (1957). At 660 MeV the $\gamma$-rays were detected by a telescope consisting of a scintillation counter and a Čerenkov counter. The scintillator was placed in anticoincidence with the plexiglass Čerenkov counter, so that only uncharged particles incident on the latter were recorded. Those $\gamma$-rays which converted in the plexiglass gave rise to an electron–photon cascade. The magnitude of this cascade, which is proportional to the number of electrons traversing the counter, and thus to its light output, gives a measure of the incident $\gamma$-ray energy. Thus at any one angle the energy spectrum of the decay $\gamma$-rays can be measured. Most measurements are made at $0°$ and $180°$, which enable the pion energy distribution in the $C$-system to be approximately determined. If some assumption is made as to the form of the pion angular distribution, the total cross-section is immediately found by integration over all angles. Alternatively, measurements may be made at the 'isotropic' angle of $\cos^{-1} 1/\sqrt{3}$;

if the angular distribution is of the form $A + \cos^2 \theta$ then it may be shown that a simple relation exists between the total cross-section and the differential cross-section at $\theta(C\text{-system}) = \cos^{-1} 1/\sqrt{3}$. Total cross-sections for neutral pion production in $p$–$p$ and $p$–'$n$' collisions between 470 and 660 MeV have been determined in this way by Prokoshkin and Typakin (1957).

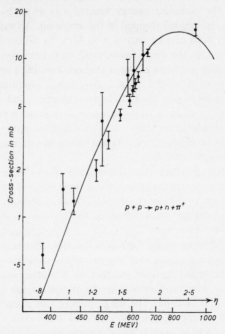

*Fig. 39. The cross-section for $p + p \rightarrow$*
*$\pi^+ + p + n$ as a function of energy*
(From MANDELSTAM. *Proc. Roy. Soc.* A244, 491 (1958))

### Total cross-section results
Characteristic experimental results for the cross-section for $p + p \rightarrow n + p + \pi^+$, as a function of energy, are shown in Fig. 39. The solid line is that calculated by Mandelstam (1958) on the

basis of the resonance hypothesis. At low energies this is largely made up of $S$-state production ($^1D_2 \rightarrow {}^3S_1p_2$ transition), but at 660 MeV the cross-section for $P$-state production is nearly twice that for $S$-state production. The agreement between theory and experiment is good up to 660 MeV. There are few data above this energy, but it is clear that the cross-section cannot continue to increase with increasing energy, for the total inelastic cross-section reaches a maximum of about 25 mb at 900 MeV and then remains approximately constant up to 2 GeV. Above 1 GeV double pion production becomes important, so that the cross-section for the process under discussion will certainly decrease with energy. Mandelstam's calculations suggest that it passes through a maximum between 700 and 800 MeV, although this prediction neglects $D$-state production which may become important at the higher energies.

The variation with energy of the total cross-section for pion production together with deuteron formation is shown in Fig. 40. The full curve is again that calculated by Mandelstam, who has included Rosenfeld's estimate of the cross-section for the non-resonant $Ss$ production, in order to extend the curve to sufficiently low energies. The theoretical curve is very largely $S$-state production; very little $P$-state production is necessary to give a good fit to the data. The theoretical curve indicates that the cross-section reaches a maximum at about 660 MeV and then decreases with increasing energy. Recent work on the reaction $\pi^+ + d \rightarrow p + p$ by Neganov and Parfenov (1958) yields data up to an equivalent incident proton energy of 900 MeV, which is in good agreement with the theoretical curve of Fig. 40. The maximum in the cross-section at 650 MeV arises because the pion is in resonance with one at the nucleons in the deuteron at this energy.

The data in Fig. 40 therefore provide strong evidence of the importance of the pion–nucleon resonance in pion production. The probability of deuteron formation is greatly reduced at high energies, for the binding energy of the deuteron (2·2 MeV) is then very small compared with the kinetic energy available for the nucleons.

The excitation function for neutral pion production has been of considerable interest from the time of the first experiments in this field. These showed that the cross-section for $\pi^0$ meson production was extremely small near to threshold; for example, Mather and Martinelli (1953) found $\sigma(\pi^0) = 0{\cdot}010$ mb at 340 MeV incident proton energy. It was realized that this fact could most readily be explained by assuming that the pion is pseudo-scalar, that is, of odd

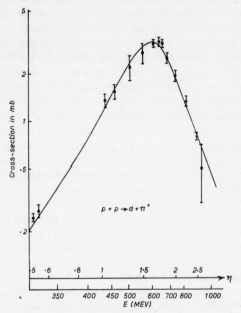

*Fig. 40. The cross-section for $p + p \rightarrow d + \pi^+$ as a function of energy*

(From MANDELSTAM. *Proc. Roy. Soc.* A244, 491 (1958), plus data of NEGANOV and PARFENOV, *J.E.T.P.* 34, 767 (1958) )

parity. The argument is that near threshold only $Ss$ transitions (in the Rosenfeld terminology) are probable, and the only transition that satisfies conservation of parity and of total angular momentum, if the pion has odd parity, is $^3P_0 \rightarrow {}^1S_0s_0$. Now the initial $^3P_0$ state has the smallest statistical weight $(2J + 1)$ of all the odd states, and further, the probability of formation of this state is not enhanced by the nucleon–nucleon interaction, as is the $^3S_1$ state. Again, from our knowledge of the scattering properties of pions, which proceeds mainly through $p$-states, one would not expect a very high probability for the production of an $s$-state meson. There is no allowed $Sp$ transition (see Table 11). Therefore, if the pion is assumed to have odd parity, the production of neutral pions near threshold will be strongly inhibited.

The actual situation is not quite as simple as the argument given above would suggest. A pion can be produced in a $p$-state relative to one of the nucleons, even though it is in an $s$-state relative to the centre of mass of the two nucleons. This possibility is termed 'displaced $s$-state production', even though it belongs to the $Ss$ transition. Similarly 'displaced $d$-state production' is possible corresponding

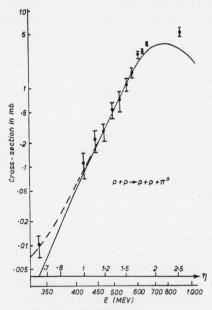

Fig. 41. The cross-section for $p + p \rightarrow$
$p + p + \pi^0$ as a function of energy

(From MANDELSTAM. Proc. Roy. Soc. A244, 491
(1958))

to an $Sd$ transition, in which the pion has angular momentum of one unit around one of the nucleons. Displaced $p$-state production is not possible, for parity cannot be conserved in this case. In Mandelstam's notation both the displaced $s$- and $d$-state production are included in the classification of $P$-state production. He finds, in fact, that these transitions dominate the production process near threshold.

The experimental data are shown in Fig. 41, which is largely based on the results of Prokoshkin and Typakin (1957). The full curve is that calculated by Mandelstam for $P$-state production; the dotted curve shows the excitation function which is obtained by including Rosenfeld's estimate of the $Ss$ production. Mandelstam finds that the displaced $s$- and $d$-state production equals the $Pp$ production at about 400 MeV; above this energy $Pp$ production predominates. The theory again predicts a maximum in the cross-section at about 700 MeV. The meagre experimental data suggests that the cross-section is approximately constant between 660 MeV and 1 GeV; for example at 925 MeV Hughes *et al.* (1957), using emulsions, find $\sigma(\pi^0) = 6 \pm 2$ mb, while at 970 MeV a diffusion cloud-chamber experiment by Batson *et al.* (1959b) gives $\sigma(\pi^0) = 5 \pm 1$ mb. Further work is clearly necessary.

*The angle and energy distributions of the pions*

We have already mentioned that all the data for the total cross-sections comes from differential measurements, that is, from observations at specified angles, or for visual techniques (except when used as counters) from observation of individual events. Near to the threshold energy it is found that the angular distribution for positive pion production has the form $1 + 3\cos^2\theta$. This is in agreement with the fact that the production occurs mainly via $S$-states (Mandelstam terminology), that is, the pions have unit angular momentum relative to the centre of mass of the two nucleons. At higher energies the distribution becomes more isotropic, particularly for the reaction $p + p \longrightarrow n + p + \pi^+$; for example, at 660 MeV Neganov and Savchenko find $d\sigma/d\Omega \propto 1 + (1\cdot32 \pm 0\cdot21)\cos^2\theta$, to be compared with $1 + 1\cdot16\cos^2\theta$ predicted by Mandelstam for $S$- and $P$-state production. The angular distribution of the pions from the reaction $p + p \longrightarrow d + \pi^+$ is of the form $1 + 0\cdot43\cos^2\theta$, and does not appear to change greatly between 460 and 660 MeV (e.g. Mescheryakov *et al.*, 1956). This is in agreement with the fact that only $S$-state production appears to be of importance up to 660 MeV.

In the case of neutral pion production, near threshold the displaced $s$- and $d$-state production ($Ss$ and $Sd$) predominates; the former gives rise to an isotropic angular distribution and the latter to a distribution of the form $1 + 3 \cos^2 \theta$. If the two types of production are assumed to occur equally, then the net angular distribution will be $1 + \cos^2 \theta$. At higher energies $Pp$ production becomes important and it turns out that the distribution then becomes more isotropic. These predictions agree quite well with the date of Prokoshkin and Typakin (1957) between 460 and 660 MeV, although the experimental errors are still rather large.

The counter experiments, and the emulsion experiment of Sidorov, yield pion energy distributions at different angles. Mescheryakov *et al.* (1956) have measured the energy spectrum of the charged mesons from $p$–$p$ collisions, at a laboratory angle of 24°. They used a strong magnetic field to give accurate momentum analysis. A typical set of results is shown in Fig. 42. The calculations of Mandelstam again appear to give a good fit to the experimental data. On the other hand, the fit is not quite so good in the case of the neutral pion energy spectrum at 0° at 660 MeV, as measured by Bayukov and Typakin (1957).

*Neutron-proton experiments and charge independence*

Pion production in $n$–$p$ collisions has not been studied in great detail, largely due to the usual difficulty of obtaining intense and monoenergetic neutron beams. The possible reactions leading to single pion production are

$$n + p \longrightarrow n + p + \pi^0 \tag{8.9}$$

$$n + p \longrightarrow d + \pi^0 \tag{8.10}$$

$$n + p \longrightarrow n + n + \pi^+ \tag{8.11}$$

and $\qquad n + p \longrightarrow p + p + \pi^- \tag{8.12}$

The reaction leading to deuteron production is of particular importance. The deuteron has isotopic spin 0, while that of the pion is 1. The isotopic spin of the final $d + \pi^0$ state can only be 1 therefore; that of the initial $n + p$ state can be 0 or 1, for the nucleons are dissimilar particles. However, in the case of the reaction $p + p \rightarrow d + \pi^+$ the initial nucleons can only be in a $T = 1$ state, and the final $d + \pi^+$ state has $T = 1$ as before. Thus, if charge independence is valid, one would expect the cross-section for the latter

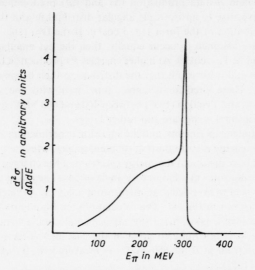

*Fig. 42. Energy spectrum of the positive pions from the reaction $p + p \rightarrow n + p + \pi^+$, at an angle of 24° in the laboratory system, and for an incident proton energy of 657 MeV*

(From MESCHERYAKOV *et al.* CERN *Symposium*, II, 347 (1956))

reaction to be twice that of the former, for the $T = 0$ initial states do not contribute to the reaction in the $n$–$p$ case. Further, the angular distribution of the pions (in the $C$-system) should be the same in the two reactions, since each reaction proceeds through the $T = 1$ isotopic spin state.

The most accurate test of these statements at the present time is afforded by the work of Flyagin *et al.* (1958) on the reaction $n + p \rightarrow \pi^0 + d$ at an effective neutron energy of 600 MeV. The authors used a counter system which allowed them to record coincidences between one of the gamma-rays from the decay of the neutral pion, and the deuteron. A scintillation counter telescope containing a lead converter was used to record the $\gamma$-quanta. The experimental results for both the differential and total cross-sections are given in Table 13 together with data for the process $p + p \longrightarrow \pi^+ + d$.

TABLE 13

| Nucleon energy in MeV | Reaction | Angular distribution | Total cross-section in mb |
|---|---|---|---|
| 580 (1) | $p + p \longrightarrow \pi^+ + d(\dagger)$ | $(0.216 \pm 0.033) + \cos^2 \theta$ | $3.10 \pm 0.24$ |
| 600 (2) | $n + p \longrightarrow \pi^0 + d$ | $(0.220 \pm 0.022) + \cos^2 \theta$ | $1.5 \pm 0.3$ |
| 633 (3) | $p + p \longrightarrow \pi^+ + d(\dagger)$ | $(0.31 \pm 0.03) + \cos^2 \theta$ | $3.05 \pm 0.23$ |
| 660 (4) | $p + p \longrightarrow \pi^+ + d$ | $(0.23 \pm 0.03) + \cos^2 \theta$ | $3.1 \pm 0.2$ |

($\dagger$) From study of $\pi^+ + d \longrightarrow p + p$; (1) Cohn (1957); (2) Flyagin *et al.* (1958); (3) Neganov and Parfenov (1958); (4) Mescheryakov and Neganov (1955).

It is clear that, within the experimental errors, the angular distributions of the pions from the two reactions are the same, and that the total cross-sections are in the ratio 2 : 1, as required by charge independence.

The reactions $p + d \longrightarrow H^3 + \pi^+$ and $p + d \longrightarrow He^3 + \pi^0$ provide, in principle, another test for the validity of the hypothesis of charge independence. The initial state has isotopic spin $T = \frac{1}{2}$, with $T_3 = +\frac{1}{2}$, for the isotopic spin of the deuteron is zero. Equation (3.18) tells us that the branching ratio of the cross-section for positive pion production to that for neutral pion production should be 2 : 1. Experimentally Crewe *et al.* (1959) obtained a value of $1.91 \pm 0.25$ for the ratio of the cross-section for the production of $H^3$ to that for the production of $He^3$.

We have already commented that the resonance model of pion production is not applicable for initial nucleon states of zero isotopic spin. Thus, if production takes place only through isobar formation; $\sigma_{01}$ will be zero. It is therefore of some interest to determine $\sigma_{01}$

as a function of energy, in order to investigate what proportion of pion production takes place through the resonant $(\frac{3}{2}, \frac{3}{2})$ state. At 400 MeV, information may be obtained from a study of the process $n + p \longrightarrow p + p + \pi^-$ or $n + n + \pi^+$, the cross-section for which is given by $\frac{1}{2}(\sigma_{11} + \sigma_{01})$. $\sigma_{11}$ is given by the $p$–$p$ data and is about 0·05 mb. At 400 MeV Yodh (1954) found the average cross-section for $\pi^+$ or $\pi^-$ meson production in $n$-$p$ collisions to be 0·16 ± 0·04 mb, which implies that $\sigma_{01} \sim 0\cdot27$ mb, to be compared with a value of $\sim 0\cdot45$ mb for $\sigma_{10}$ at the same energy. At 580 MeV there now exists a complete set of data for pion production in both $p$–$p$ and $n$–$p$ collisions. The cross-section for neutral pion production in $n$–$p$ collisions is $5\cdot7 \pm 1\cdot5$ mb (Dzhelepov et al., 1955), while for charged pion production it is $2\cdot2 \pm 0\cdot44$ mb (Kazarinov and Simonov, 1958). $\sigma_{11}$ is known from the $p$–$p$ data. Thus $\sigma_{01} = 2 \sigma(n + p \longrightarrow \pi^+) - \sigma_{11} = 2\cdot4 \pm 0\cdot9$ mb. It is also of interest to calculate the total cross-section for pion production from initial $T = 0$ states, which may be denoted by $\sigma_0^\pi$. We have

$$\sigma(n + p \longrightarrow \pi^\pm, \pi^0) = \tfrac{1}{2}\sigma_1^\pi + \tfrac{1}{2}\sigma_0^\pi$$

and

$$\sigma(n + p \longrightarrow \pi^\pm, \pi^0) = 2\sigma(n + p \longrightarrow \pi^+) + \sigma(n + p \longrightarrow \pi^0)$$

The $p$–$p$ data give $\sigma_1^\pi = 10\cdot7 \pm 0\cdot73$ mb, while the experimental data for the $n$–$p$ reactions are given above; substitution yields $\sigma_0^\pi = 9\cdot3 \pm 3\cdot7$ mb. Thus, at energies close to 600 MeV, transitions which lead to pion production occur with equal probability from initial nucleon states of $T = 0$ and $T = 1$. This is in apparent contradiction with the fact that there is known to be a resonance interaction in the $T = 1$ state of pion and nucleon, whereas no such interaction has been suggested for the $T = 0$ state at low energies.

At higher energies the experimental data are rather meagre. One interesting experiment is that of Batson et al. (1959a) who have investigated $p$-'$n$' interactions in a diffusion cloud chamber filled with deuterium. The incident proton energy was 970 MeV. Some 200 $p$-'$n$' events were observed, although not all could be unambiguously identified. The measured cross-sections for neutral and charged pion production appear to be inconsistent with the relations given in Table 11. Assuming that charge independence is valid, the measured cross-section for $n + p \longrightarrow p + p + \pi^-$ leads to $\sigma_{01}$

$= 0.2 \pm 1.3$ mb. On the other hand, taking $\sigma(n + p \longrightarrow n + p + \pi^0)$ as the primary data, then $\sigma_{01} = 16 \pm 7$ mb. Clearly further work is required in this energy region, and there is a particular need for experiments which can provide direct checks on the hypothesis of charge independence.

## Pion production at energies above 700 MeV

### Theories

One might expect that statistical ideas could be applied to describe the pion production process at energies at which a considerable amount of energy is available for meson production in the $C$-system of two colliding nucleons. A theory of this type was put forward by Fermi (1950, 1953), who made the basic assumptions ($a$), that there is a collection of energy in a small volume for a short space of time and ($b$) that the energy is then distributed amongst the various degrees of freedom of the system according to statistical laws. By degrees of freedom one means the various possible pion and nucleon states. Allowance is made for the facts that ($a$) some particles may be identical (Pauli principle), ($b$) the multiplicity of spin states, and ($c$) the conservation laws must be obeyed. The adjustable parameter of the theory is the volume $\Omega$ into which the energy is confined; the size of $\Omega$ is usually taken to be of the order of $\hbar/m_\pi c$.

This theory has been modified by Belenkii and Nikishov (1955) and by Kovacs (1956) to include the final state interactions between the particles and, in particular (i) the pion–nucleon interaction in the $T = J = \frac{3}{2}$ resonant state, and (ii) the nucleon–nucleon interaction. Kovacs assumed that the nucleons were always in a relative $S$-state; this assumption is very restrictive since it leads to the prediction of zero neutral pion production in $p$–$p$ collisions (see equation 8.7).

In contrast to the Fermi theory one may assume that the pion production always proceeds by the excitation of one or both nucleons to an isobaric state. At low energies a picture of this type gives a good representation of the data. Detailed calculations of the characteristics of the meson production predicted by an isobar model have been made by Lindenbaum and Sternheimer (1957), for energies between 800 MeV and 3 GeV. The primary assumption made by these authors was that the relative probability for any final state was proportional to a momentum space factor multiplied by the relative probability for the formation of one, or two, isobaric states. The probability for isobar formation can be related to the known variation with energy of the $\pi^+ + p$ scattering cross-section. Consider, as an example, the excitation of one nucleon, which subsequently decays into a proton and a positive pion. This may be written as

$$p + p \longrightarrow p^* + n \quad (T = J = \tfrac{3}{2})$$

and $$p^* \longrightarrow p + \pi^+ + Q \tag{8.13}$$

where $Q$ is the kinetic energy of the two particles in the isobar rest-system, and which has a distribution similar to the $\pi^+ + p$ excitation function, with a maximum at 154 MeV ($C$-system). For a given incident proton energy, the range of possible $Q$ values will be determined by the amount of energy available. If the pion production is governed by statistical factors alone, as in the Fermi theory, the distribution of $Q$ values obtained will vary greatly with the energy of the experiment. (Note that $Q$ may always be defined, as in (8.13), and a value of $Q$ may be calculated, irrespective of whether or not the production does take place through an intermediate isobaric state.) On the other hand production via an isobaric state should always give a $Q$-value distribution peaked around 150 MeV. Further, in the rest-system of the isobar the proton and the pion will travel in opposite directions to each other; if the velocity of the isobar, in the $C$-system of all the final state particles, is not too high, then this correlation should still be observable in the $C$-system. The Fermi theory will also give rise to an angular correlation, due solely to considerations of momentum conservation. The important point is that the Fermi theory predicts an angular correlation and a $Q$-value distribution which will be the same for $p$ and $\pi^+$ and $n$ and $\pi^+$, whereas the isobar picture predicts that there should be a marked difference between the distribution for $p\pi^+$ and that for $n\pi^{+\cdot}$ This comes about because the formation of a $T = \tfrac{3}{2}$, $J = \tfrac{3}{2}$ state in $p$–$p$ collisions occurs in a $p\pi^+$ system in $\tfrac{9}{10}$ of the cases, and in an $n\pi^+$ system in $\tfrac{1}{10}$ of the cases.

*Experimental studies of single pion production above 700 MeV*

Relatively few experiments on the characteristics of pion production have been carried out at high energies, using the proton and neutron beams from accelerators. We shall not discuss here the extensive cosmic-ray work using nuclear emulsions which, in general, relates to collisions with complex nuclei, and to energies of many GeV (see, for example, Hooper and Scharff (1958)). In the majority of accelerator experiments a visual technique has been used, usually that of the hydrogen-filled diffusion chamber, although isolated expansion chamber and nuclear emulsion experiments have been carried out.

At energies up to 1 GeV single pion production is predominant in $p$–$p$ collisions, via reactions (8.1), (8.2) and (8.3) with (8.1) being the most important. At 1·5 GeV about 20% of the inelastic cross-section corresponds to double pion production, and at 2·7 GeV the estimated single to double to triple meson production ratio is 36 : 48 : 16. The many different production processes which are possible when multiple production becomes important makes the identification of many events very difficult. We shall not consider the question of the multiple production of pions, for it is beyond the scope of this book.

At energies up to 2 GeV the most extensive $p$–$p$ and $n$–$p$ data comes from a series of diffusion-chamber experiments carried out using the proton synchrotrons at Birmingham and at Brookhaven (e.g. Batson *et al.*, 1959b, who give references to the earlier work). $Q$-value distributions, angular correlation plots, and angular and momentum distributions of the emitted particles, have been obtained from these experiments and compared with the predictions of the statistical theory and of the isobar theory. The comparison is made difficult by the relatively small number of events suitable for analysis. In general the predictions of the isobar theory agree better with the data than the predictions of the statistical theory (see Lindenbaum and Sternheimer, 1957). As an example of this statement the $Q$-value plot between proton and $\pi^+$, obtained by Batson *et al.* at 970 MeV, is shown in Fig. 43. It can be seen that the results are in reasonable agreement with the predictions of the isobar theory.

The present situation is best summarized by the statement that in general the isobar model seems to give a better fit to the experimental data than the pure statistical theory, although the modified form of the statistical theory due to Kovacs does give a good account

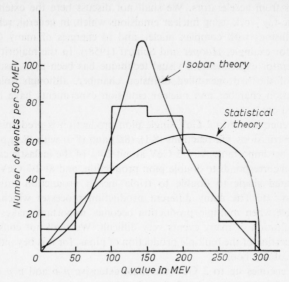

*Fig. 43. The Q-value distribution for proton and $\pi^+$, for events of type $p + p \to n + p + \pi^+$ at an incident proton energy of 970 MeV*

(From BATSON *et al. Proc. Roy. Soc.* A251, 218 (1959))

of the $n$–$p$ data between 1 and 2 GeV. Much more information is required before a clear description can be given of the mechanism of pion production at energies in the GeV range.

## BIBLIOGRAPHY

BETHE, H. A. and DE HOFFMANN, F. 1955. *Mesons and Fields*, **II.** *Mesons*. Sections 48, 49.

FERMI, E. 1955. *Nuovo Cimento*, **II,** Supplemento No. 1, 63.

GELL-MANN, M. and WATSON, K. M. 1954. *Ann. Rev. Nuc. Sci.* **4,** 219.

LINDENBAUM, S. J. 1957. *Ann. Rev. Nuc. Sci.* **7,** 317.

# REFERENCES

ALSTON, M. H., CREWE, A. V., EVANS, W. H. and VON GIERKE, G. 1956. *Proc. Phys. Soc.* **A69**, 691.

BATSON, A. P., CULWICK, B. B., KLEPP, H. and RIDDIFORD, L. 1959a. *Proc. Roy. Soc.* **A251**, 233.

BATSON, A. P., CULWICK, B. B., HILL, J. G. and RIDDIFORD, L. 1959b. *Proc. Roy. Soc.* **A251**, 218.

BAYUKOV, Y. D. and TYPAKIN, A. A. 1958. *JETP.* **32**, 953 (*S.P.* (*JETP.*) **5**, 779, 1955).

BELENKII, S. Z. and NIKISHOV, A. I. 1955. *JETP.* **28**, 744 (*S.P.* (*JETP.*) **1**, 593, 1955).

BRUECKNER, K. A. 1952. *Phys. Rev.* **86**, 106.

BRUECKNER, K. A. and WATSON, K. M. 1951. *Phys. Rev.* **83**, 1; 1952. ibid. **86**, 923.

COHN, C. E. 1957. *Phys. Rev.* **105**, 1582.

CREWE, A. V., GARWIN, E., LEDLEY, B., LILLETHUN, E., MARCH, R. and MARCOWITZ, S. 1959. *Phys. Rev. Letters*, **2**, 269.

DZHELEPOV, V. P., OGANESYAN, K. O. and FLYAGIN, V. B. 1955. *JETP.* **29**, 886 (*S.P.* (*JETP.*) **2**, 757, 1956).

FERMI, E. 1950. *Prog. Theor. Phys.* **5**, 570; 1953. *Phys. Rev.* **92**, 452.

FLYAGIN, V. B., DZHELEPOV, V. P., KISELEV, V. S. and OGANESYAN, K. O. 1958. *JETP.* **35**, 854 (*S.P.* (*JETP.*) **8**, 592, 1959).

HOOPER, J. E. and SCHARFF, M. 1958. *The Cosmic Radiation.* Ch. IV. Methuen.

HUGHES, I. S., MARCH, P. V., MUIRHEAD, H. and LOCK, W. O. 1957. *Phil. Mag.* **2** (*Ser.* 8), 215.

KAZARINOV, YU. M. and SIMONOV, YU. N. 1958. *JEPT*, **35**, 78 (*S.P.* (*JETP*) **8**, 56, 1959).

KOVACS, J. S. 1956. *Phys. Rev.* **101**, 397.

LINDENBAUM, S. J. and STERNHEIMER, R. M. 1957. *Phys. Rev.* **105**, 1814.

LINDENBAUM, S. J. and YUAN, L. C. 1954. *Phys. Rev.* **93**, 901, 1431.

MANDELSTAM, S. 1958. *Proc. Roy. Soc.* **A244**, 491.

MATHER, J. W. and MARTINELLI, E. A. 1953. *Phys. Rev.* **92**, 780.

MESCHERYAKOV, M. G., BOGACHEV, N. P. and NEGANOV, B. S. 1956a. *Nuovo Cimento*, **III**, Supplemento No. 1, 119.

MESCHERYAKOV, M. G., ZRELOV, V. P., NEGANOV, B. S., VZOROV, I. K. and SHABUDIN, A. F. 1956b. *CERN Symposium*, II, 347.

MESCHERYAKOV, M. G. and NEGANOV, B. S. 1955. *Dokl. Akad. Nauk SSSR.* **100**, 677.

NEGANOV, B. S. and SAVCHENKO, O. V. 1957. *JETP.* **32**, 1265 (*S.P.* (*JETP.*) **5**, 1033, 1957).

NEGANOV, B. S. and PARFENOV, L. B. 1958. *JETP.* **34**, 767 (*S.P.* (*JETP.*) **3**, 528, 1958).

PEASLEE, D. C. 1954. *Phys. Rev.* **94**, 1085; ibid. **95**, 1580.

PROKOSHKIN, YU. D. and TYPAKIN, A. A. 1957. *JETP.* **32**, 750 (*S.P.* (*JETP.*) **5**, 618, 1957).

ROSENFELD, A. H. 1954. *Phys. Rev.* **96**, 139.

SIDOROV, V. M. 1956. *CERN Symposium*, II, 366.

YUAN, L. C. and LINDENBAUM, S. J. 1956. *Phys. Rev.* **103**, 404.

YODH, G. B. 1955. *Phys. Rev.* **98**, 1330.

# Appendix I

To describe the quantized field, consider, as a simple example, the case of the harmonic oscillator. This has an energy, written in Hamiltonian form of

$$H = \frac{1}{2}\frac{p^2}{m} + \frac{1}{2}m\omega^2 x^2$$

where $p$ is the momentum of the particle of mass $m$ oscillating in the $x$-direction with frequency $\omega$. The Schrödinger equation is obtained by putting $p = -i\hbar\,\partial/\partial x$, viz

$$\left(-\frac{\hbar^2}{2m}\nabla^2 + \frac{1}{2}m\omega^2 x^2 - E\right)\Psi = 0$$

This equation has solutions which are Hermite polynomials, the energy levels being given by

$$E_n = \hbar\omega(n + \tfrac{1}{2})$$

where $n$ is an integer.

Now in discussing the harmonic oscillator one introduces operators $a$ and $a^*$ defined by

$$a = \left(\frac{1}{2m\hbar\omega}\right)^{\frac{1}{2}}\left(p - im\omega x\right) \tag{A.1}$$

and

$$a^* = \left(\frac{1}{2m\hbar\omega}\right)^{\frac{1}{2}}\left(p + im\omega x\right) \tag{A.2}$$

Replacing $p$ by $-i\hbar\partial/\partial x$, $a$ and $a^*$ may be written

$$a = \beta\left(\frac{\partial}{\partial x} + \frac{m\omega}{\hbar}x\right)$$

and

$$a^* = \beta\left(\frac{\partial}{\partial x} - \frac{m\omega}{\hbar}x\right)$$

where

$$\beta = -i\hbar\left(\frac{1}{2m\hbar\omega}\right)^{\frac{1}{2}}$$

185

If the state whose energy is $(n + \frac{1}{2})\hbar\omega$ is represented by a state function $\Psi_n$, it is readily shown (e.g. Schiff, pp. 60 seq.) that

$$a^*\Psi_n = n^{\frac{1}{2}}\Psi_{n+1}$$

and

$$a\Psi_{n+1} = n^{\frac{1}{2}}\Psi_n$$

For example, consider the ground state $\Psi_0 = e^{-\frac{1}{2}\alpha^2x^2}$ where $\alpha^2 = m\omega/\hbar$, then

$$a^*\Psi_0 = \beta\Big(\frac{\partial}{\partial x} - \alpha^2 x\Big) \exp\left(- \tfrac{1}{2}\alpha^2x^2\right) = - \alpha^2\beta x \exp\left(- \tfrac{1}{2}\alpha^2x^2\right)$$

and $x \exp\left(- \tfrac{1}{2}\alpha^2x^2\right)$ is proportional to $\Psi_1$ apart from a constant

so that

$$a^*\Psi_0 = \Psi_1$$

whereas

$$a\Psi_0 = 0$$

For this reason the operators $a$ and $a^*$ are known as annihilation and creation operators, respectively, since they decrease or increase the number of quanta in the state by one unit.

The commutation rule $[x, p] = i\hbar$ becomes

$$[a,a^*] = 1 \tag{A.3}$$

Therefore the operator $a^*$ can be said to create an energy of $\hbar\omega$ whereas $a$ annihilates an energy of $\hbar\omega$. In terms of $a$, $a^*$ it is not difficult to show that

$$H = \hbar\omega aa^* + \frac{\hbar\omega}{2}$$

*Meson fields*

Let us consider the bearing that this example has on the fields in which we are interested. The energy of the electromagnetic field, $\frac{1}{8\pi}\int(E^2 + H^2)d^3x$ can be transformed into

$$\frac{1}{8\pi}\int \Big(\frac{1}{c^2}\Big(\frac{\partial A_\mu}{\partial t}\Big)^2 + (\nabla A_\mu)^2\Big)d^3x$$

where $A_\mu$ is the vector potential discussed on page 47.
In the same way the energy of the pion field can be written

$$= \int \Big(\frac{1}{c^2}\Big(\frac{\partial\phi}{\partial t}\Big)^2 + (\nabla\phi)^2 + \frac{m^2c^2}{\hbar^2}\phi^2\Big)d^3x \tag{A.4}$$

This expression will be familiar from sound wave theory, or from the theory of a vibrating string, which, if its displacement is $\zeta$ on the $x$, $y$ plane, has an energy of

$$\int \left( \frac{1}{c^2}\left(\frac{\partial \zeta}{\partial t}\right)^2 + \left(\frac{\partial \zeta}{\partial x}\right)^2 + \left(\frac{\partial \zeta}{\partial y}\right)^2 \right) dx\, dy$$

but there is the extra term $(mc\phi/\hbar)^2$ in (A.4) which corresponds to the mass of the field quanta in the relativistic theory. The relevance of the harmonic oscillator to this discussion is that if $\phi(x,t)$ is considered decomposed into its Fourier amplitudes

$$\phi(x,t) = \sum e^{ikx}\phi(k,t)$$

then for, say, a neutral field one obtains for the energy

$$\int d^3k \left\{ \frac{1}{c^2}\left(\frac{\partial \phi}{\partial t}\right)^2 (k,t) + \left( k^2 + \left(\frac{mc}{\hbar}\right)^2 \right)\phi^2(k,t) \right\} \qquad \text{(A.5}$$

But the energy of the harmonic oscillator is just $\dfrac{m}{2}\left(\dfrac{\partial x}{\partial t}\right)^2 + m\omega^2 x^2$, so that each $\phi(k,t)$ may be thought of as the coordinate of an harmonic oscillator, labelled with $k$, whose frequency depends upon $k$. Creation and annihilation operators $a_k, \bar{a}_k$ can be introduced by writing

$$\phi(x,t) = \int \frac{d^3k}{(2\pi)^{\frac{3}{2}}} \sqrt{\frac{1}{2\omega_k}} \left[ a_k e^{i(\mathbf{kx}-\omega_k t)} + \bar{a}_k e^{-i(\mathbf{kx}-\omega_k t)} \right] \qquad [\text{(A.6)}$$

where $\omega_k$ is the total energy, and where a covariant normalization has been used. $\phi$ itself may therefore be regarded as an operator, since it is a combination of the operators $a_k$, $\bar{a}_k$. The commutators of the $a$'s corresponding to different $k$ are taken to be zero. The commutator $(a_k, \bar{a}_k)$ is that given in (A.3). The total energy of the field is then obtained from (A.5), with the form

$$\int d^3k\; \bar{a}_k a_k \omega_k = \int d^3k\; N_k \omega_k$$

For a charged field the development proceeds in a similar manner, except that $\phi$ is taken to be complex, with $\phi_+ = \phi_1 + i\phi_2$ and $\phi_- = \phi_1 - i\phi_2$ (see p. 38). Creation and annihilation operators are introduced in the expressions

$$\phi = \int \frac{d^3k}{(2\pi)^{\frac{3}{2}}} \sqrt{\frac{1}{2\omega_k}} \left[ b_k \, e^{i(\mathbf{kx} - \omega_k t)} + \bar{a}_k e^{-i(\mathbf{kx} - \omega_k t)} \right] \tag{A.7}$$

and $\quad \phi^* = \int \frac{d^3k}{(2\pi)^{\frac{3}{2}}} \sqrt{\frac{1}{2\omega_k}} \left[ \bar{b}_k \, e^{i(\mathbf{kx} - \omega_k t)} + a_k e^{-i(\mathbf{kx} - \omega_k t)} \right] \tag{A.8}$

Again all combinations of the $a$'s and $b$'s give zero for their commutation relations except $[\bar{a}_k, a_k]$ and $[\bar{b}_k, b_k]$ which behave as (A.3). $\phi$ is associated with the creation of positive mesons (via $a_k$) or the annihilation of negative mesons (via $b_k$) and similarly for $\phi^*$; these operators have been used in this way on pages 40–41. In other words $a_k$ acts on the wave function which says that the pions are in the ground state with zero total energy (i.e. a meson vacuum), and generates a pion of momentum $k$. This is exactly analogous to operating with $a^*$ on the ground state of the harmonic oscillator to generate the first excited state. The energy of the meson field is the sum of the numbers of mesons of momentum $k$ times the energy of one such meson $\sqrt{k^2 + m^2}$ that is,

$$H = \int d^3k [N_k^+ \omega_k + N_k^- \omega_k]$$

$$= \int d^3k [\bar{a}a\omega_k + \bar{b}b\omega_k]$$

It can also be shown directly that the charge of the system

$$Q = \int d^3k (\bar{a}a - \bar{b}b) = \int d^3k (N^+ - N^-)$$

where $N^+$ is the number of positive mesons and $N^-$ is the number of negative mesons.

In the above discussion a bar over a letter, or an asterisk, indicates the complex conjugate.

# Index